NATIONAL GEOGRAPHIC
Reach
for Reading

COMMON CORE PROGRAM

NATIONAL GEOGRAPHIC LEARNING | CENGAGE Learning

Acknowledgments

Grateful acknowledgment is given to the authors, artists, photographers, museums, publishers, and agents for permission to reprint copyrighted material. Every effort has been made to secure the appropriate permission. If any omissions have been made or if corrections are required, please contact the Publisher.

Cover illustration: Joel Sotelo

Cover Design and Art Direction: Visual Asylum

Illustration Credits: All PM illustrations by National Geographic Learning.

For product information and technology assistance, contact us at
Customer & Sales Support, 888-915-3276

For permission to use material from this text or product, submit all requests online at **www.cengage.com/permissions**
Further permissions questions can be emailed to
permissionrequest@cengage.com

National Geographic Learning | Cengage Learning
1 Lower Ragsdale Drive
Building 1, Suite 200
Monterey, CA 93940

Cengage Learning is a leading provider of customized learning solutions with office locations around the globe, including Singapore, the United Kingdom, Australia, Mexico, Brazil, and Japan. Locate your local office at **www.cengage.com/global**.

Cengage Learning products are represented in Canada by Nelson Education, Ltd.

Visit National Geographic Learning online at **NGL.Cengage.com**
Visit our corporate website a **www.cengage.com**

Printed in the USA.
Quad/Graphics, Versailles, KY

ISBN: 978-13054-99010 (Practice Book)

ISBN: 978-13056-58714 (Practice Masters)

Teachers are authorized to reproduce the practice masters in this book in limited quantity and solely for use in their own classrooms.

Printed in the United States of America

18 19 20 21 22 23 24

13 12 11 10 9 8

Contents

Unit 1: Hello, Neighbor!

Unit 2: Staying Alive

Unit 3: Water for Everyone

Unit 4: Lend a Hand

Name _____ Date _____

Short *a*

Circle the word that names the picture.

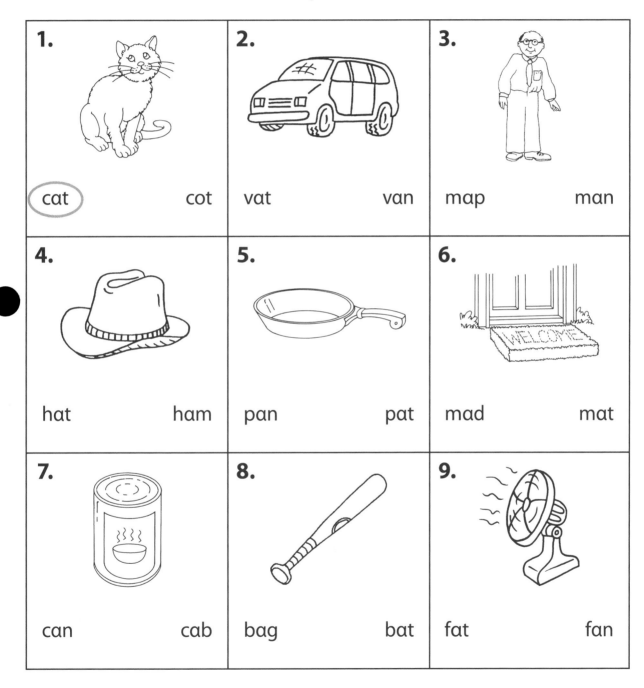

1.

cat   cot

2.

vat   van

3.

map   man

4.

hat   ham

5.

pan   pat

6.

mad   mat

7.

can   cab

8.

bag   bat

9.

fat   fan

Read It Together Find a hat and a pan.

For use with TE p. T3c   **PM1.1**   Unit 1 | Hello, Neighbor!

Name _____ Date _____

Character

Make a character map for Jae and Vera from the song "Our Hometown Workers."

Character	Who the Character Is	What the Character's Job Is

 Share your character map with a partner.

Name _____ Date _____

Short *a*

Write the word that completes each sentence.

1. ran   cat

I have a _____ .

2. lap   tap

The cat is on my _____ .

3. hat   pat

I like to _____ my cat.

4. mat   van

Dad is in the _____ .

5. map   fat

Dad has a _____ in the van.

6. can   bat

The map _____ help him.

7. mat   ran

Can you see the _____ ?

8. rat   tan

The mat is _____ .

9. sat   yam

Jan _____ on the mat.

Name _____ Date _____

Final -s

Write the word that completes each sentence.

1. pal   pals

Dad and Al are _____ .

2. his   has

Al _____ a van.

3. is   as

Al _____ in the van.

4. cap   caps

I see _____ in the van, too.

5. find   finds

Al _____ a tan cap!

6. like   likes

Dad _____ my tan cap.

7. hat   hats

Al and I find a _____ for Dad.

8. is   his

It _____ tan.

9. as   has

Dad _____ a tan hat, and I have a tan cap!

For use with TE p. T6f   **PM1.4**   Unit 1 | Hello, Neighbor!

High Frequency Words

Trace each High Frequency Word and then write it.

day day

there there

do do

what what

help help

by by

then then

people people

For use with TE p. T6f   **PM1.5**   **Unit 1** | Hello, Neighbor!

● Word Cards: Words with Short *a*, Final *-s*

cat	bat	ax	van
maps	ham	man	hat
at	laps	ban	ran
Max	am	traps	dad
tax	mad	slaps	pan
fan	wax	yam	swam
back	caps	flat	sacks

● High Frequency Word Cards

I	see
too	what
have	help
a	people
the	do
my	there
is	by
on	day
it	then

PM1.7

Name _____   Date _____

Short *i*

Circle the word that names the picture.

1.	2.	3.
pan (pin)	pig pat	cat kid
4.	5.	6.
fin fan	wax wig	six sat
7.	8.	9.
lap lip	bib bat	bat bib

Read It Together   Where is the pig? Where is the bib?

For use with TE p. T9c   **PM1.8**   Unit 1 | Hello, Neighbor!

High Frequency Words

Max and His Cat

Write a word from the box to complete each sentence.

High Frequency **Words**
by
day
do
help
people
then
there
what

1. Max and his cat have a big _____ !

2. Max sees his cat go _____ him.

3. _____ Max cannot see his cat!

4. Where is his cat? It is up _____ !

5. _____ can Max do?

6. He can find _____ to help!

● Word Cards: Plural Nouns

s	es	y	i + es
box	cat	church	glass
branch	library	lunch	farm
bush	town	park	dish
office	potato	community	place
home	hospital	city	school
store	address	sandwich	road
crash	pony	beach	walk
story	wind	berry	tree

Phonics

Short *i*

Write the word that completes each sentence.

1. **six   sax**

   I have _____ pigs.

2. **had   hid**

   That pig _____ by the bin.

3. **did   dad**

   I _____ find it there!

4. **hit   hat**

   The little pig sat on my tan _____ !

5. **big   bag**

   This pig is not little. It is _____ .

6. **pat   pit**

   I like to _____ this pig.

7. **It   At**

   _____ likes that!

8. **as   is**

   That pig _____ not my pig.

9. **his   has**

   It is _____ pig!

Phonics

Possessives

Write the word that completes each sentence.

1. Dan   Dan's

This is _____ cat.

2. Pat   Pat's

The cat is in _____ hat.

3. cat   cat's

The _____ naps in the hat!

4. kids   kids'

I see the _____ cats, too.

5. pals   pals'

The cats are in the _____ laps.

6. cats   cats'

The _____ nap in the laps.

7. Dad   Dad's

Where is _____ cat?

8. cats   cats'

It is not on the _____ mat.

9. Kim   Kim's

It naps in _____ cap!

Grammar and Writing

Write Plural Nouns

Read the story. Then choose a word from the box that goes with each sentence and make it plural.

glass	box	party
hat	game	hutch

Last summer, I went to three __parties__. At

one party, we made a big fort out of cardboard

_____. We played fun _____ at every party.

At Robert's party, we drank apple juice out of cool

red _____. At Sarah's party, we got to take her pet

rabbits out of their _____. The thing I remember

most about Kareem's party is the crazy paper

_____ we wore.

For use with TE p. T1m   **PM1.13**   **Unit 1** | Hello, Neighbor!

Name _____ Date _____

Quinito's Neighborhood

Make a character map for the people in "Quinito's Neighborhood."

Character	Who the Character Is	What the Character's Job Is
Mami and Papi	Quinito's parents	She is a carpenter. He is a nurse.
Guillermo	Quinito's neighbor	
Dona Estrella		She is a seamstress.

 Use your character map to describe the characters in "Quinito's Neighborhood" to a partner.

Name _____   Date _____

Phonics

Short o

Circle the word that names the picture.

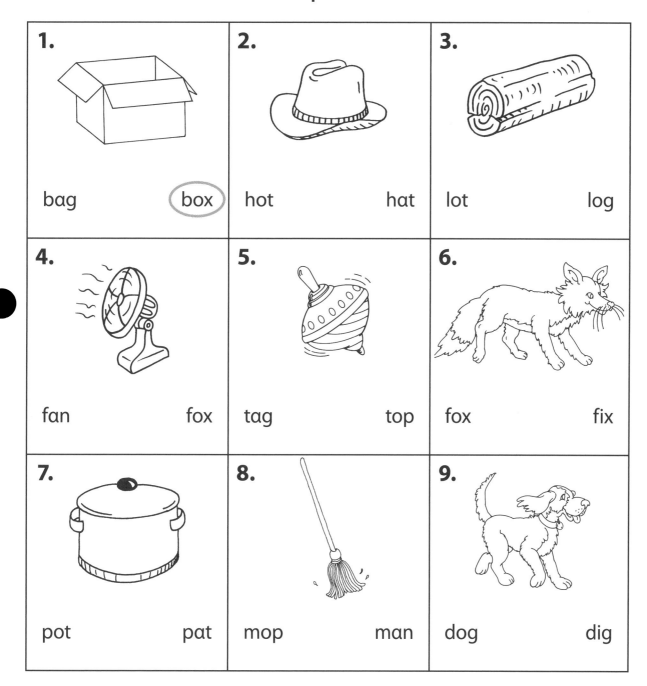

1.	**2.**	**3.**
bag (box)	hot hat	lot log
4.	**5.**	**6.**
fan fox	tag top	fox fix
7.	**8.**	**9.**
pot pat	mop man	dog dig

Read It Together What can fit in a box?

For use with TE p. T25o   **PM1.15**   Unit 1 | Hello, Neighbor!

Phonics

Short o

Write the word that completes each sentence.

1. dig   dog

Jax is my _____ .

2. big   bog

He is _____ and tan.

3. jig   jog

Jax and I like to _____ .

4. log   lag

We see a _____ by the bog.

5. hat   hot

Jax is _____ .

6. hips   hops

Jax _____ on the log.

7. top   tap

He sits on _____ .

8. fix   fox

Look! A _____ comes out!

9. on   an

Jax and I jog _____ !

Name _____   Date _____

Syllables

Circle the word that names the picture.

1. pit / (pig)	**2.** cat / cot	**3.** dog / dig
4. six / sax	**5.** log / lot	**6.** mop / map
7. on / ox	**8.** fan / fin	**9.** wag / wig
10. pin / pan	**11.** ax / at	**12.** hot / hat

Read It Together   A dog can dig. Can you dig, too?

PM1.17   Unit 1 | Hello, Neighbor!

Handwriting

High Frequency Words

Trace each High Frequency Word and then write it.

come come

from from

her her

look look

of of

one one

out out

some some

● Word Cards: Words with Short *o*

lock	top	pot	cob
sob	mop	spot	dot
sock	con	Tom	job
● flock	lot	hop	rob
rock	rot	blob	stop
lob	hot	pop	flop
● cotton	dock	bottom	Ron

For use with TE p. T25g   **PM1.19**   **Unit 1** | Hello, Neighbor!

● High Frequency Word Cards

you	are
all	of
not	out
here	one
find	some
his	from
and	come
where	her
little	look

For use with TE p. T25g   **PM1.20**   Unit 1 | Hello, Neighbor!

Name _____   Date _____

Compare Genres

Show how realistic fiction and a photo-essay are different.

Realistic Fiction	Photo-Essay
• tells about things that could really happen	• uses photographs and text to tell about a topic

 Take turns with a partner. Give information about a story or a photo-essay.

Phonics

Syllable Division

Divide each word into syllables. Circle the word that names the picture.

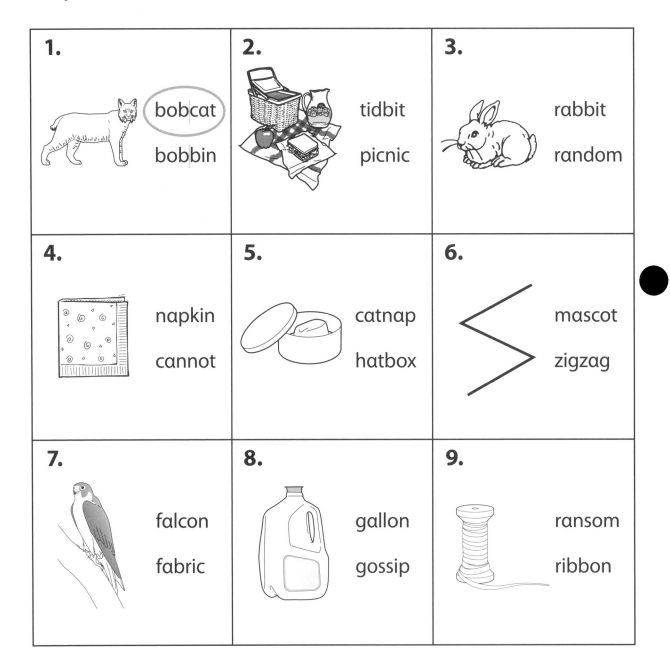

1.	2.	3.
bob|cat bob|bin	tidbit picnic	rabbit random
4.	**5.**	**6.**
napkin cannot	catnap hatbox	mascot zigzag
7.	**8.**	**9.**
falcon fabric	gallon gossip	ransom ribbon

Read It Together Do you see a bobcat or a napkin at a picnic?

● **High Frequency Words**

Hats in a Box

Write a word from the box to complete each sentence.

High Frequency Words
come
from
her
look
of
one
out
some

_____
- -

1. Jan got this hatbox _____ her attic.

●
_____
- -

2. Come _____ at it.

_____
- -

3. There are _____ hats in the box!

_____
- -

4. _____ hat has ribbons.

_____
- -

5. A lot _____ the ribbons are big!

_____
- -

● **6.** Look! That hat is _____ of the box and on Jan!

Grammar: Plural Nouns

Use Plural Nouns

1. Take turns with a partner.

2. Toss a marker onto the game board.

3. Follow the directions in the square you land on.

4. After you say your sentence, your partner says a sentence with a different noun of the same type.

Say a sentence with a plural noun that ends in **s**.	Say a sentence with a plural noun that changes its spelling.
Say a sentence with a plural noun that ends in **es**.	Say a sentence with a plural noun that does not change its form.
Say a sentence with a plural noun that ends in **ies**.	Say a sentence with a collective noun.

Name _____   Date _____

Syllable Division

Divide the words into syllables. Write the word that completes each sentence.

1. **picnic   gallon**

   Mom, Dad, Ron, and Ron's dog are on a _____ .

2. **canyon   catnap**

   Ron's dog, Sam, had a _____ . Then he got up.

3. **cannot   bobcat**

   Sam _____ sit. He digs!

4. **napkin   attic**

   He digs up one _____ .

5. **zigzag   ribbon**

   He digs up some _____ .

6. **admit   fabric**

   He finds some tan _____ , too.

7. **fossil   gossip**

   Look! Sam digs up a _____ !

8. **gallon   rabbit**

   It is not from a _____ .

9. **tidbit   bobcat**

   It is from a _____ !

Write Plural and Collective Nouns

Read the story. Then choose a word from the box that goes with each sentence and make it plural if necessary.

lunch	baby	fish
man	family	park

Our neighborhood has two great ___parks___ kids can play in. One park has a big pond. You can see lots of moms and dads there pushing their new _____ in strollers. They like to look at the _____ that swim in the pond. One _____ had a picnic on Saturday. The parents and kids ate their _____ sitting under a big maple tree. After they left, two _____ sat under the tree and played guitars.

Name _____ Date _____

Grammar: Plural Nouns

Say Plural Nouns

1. **Play with a partner.**

2. **Spin the spinner.**

3. **Change the noun to a plural noun.**

4. **Say a sentence using the plural noun.**

Make a Spinner

1. Put a paper clip ⊂⊐ in the center of the circle.

2. Hold one end of the paper clip with a pencil.

3. Spin the paper clip around the pencil.

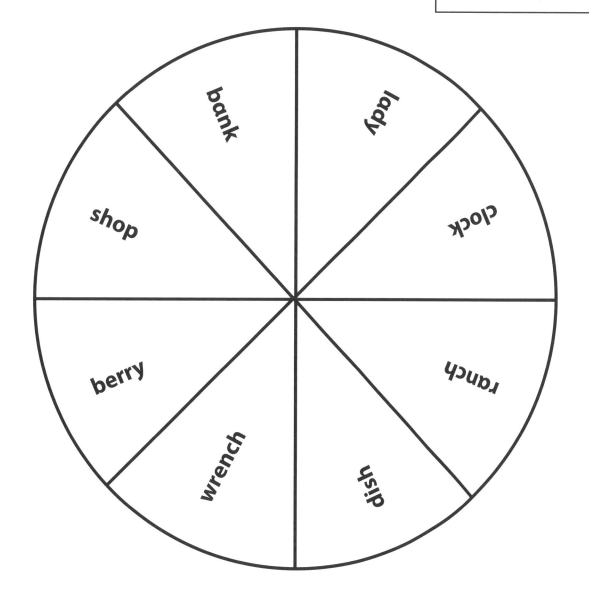

Name _____   Date _____

Phonics

Short e

Circle the word that names the picture.

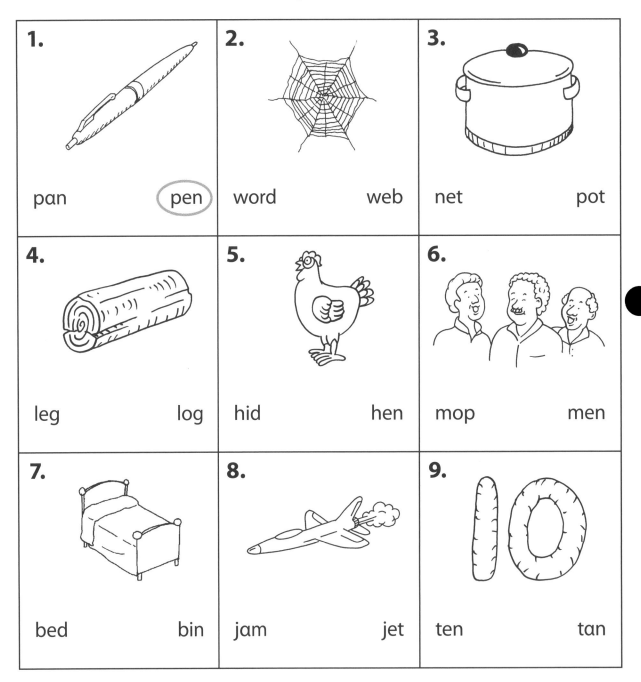

1.	**2.**	**3.**
pan (pen)	word web	net pot
4.	**5.**	**6.**
leg log	hid hen	mop men
7.	**8.**	**9.**
bed bin	jam jet	ten tan

Read It Together   Ten men get the ten jets.

© National Geographic Learning, a part of Cengage Learning, Inc.
For use with TE p. T31q   **PM1.28**

Name _____ Date _____

●

Our Community

Make a details cluster to tell about places in your community.

●

 Share your details cluster with a partner. Find out which places you both enjoy in your community.

For use with TE p. T33a   **PM1.29**   Unit 1 | Hello, Neighbor!

Phonics

Short e

Write the word that completes each sentence.

1. den   din

What do you see come out of its _____ ?

2. rid   red

It is a _____ fox.

3. pat   pet

This fox is not a _____ .

4. hen   happen

The fox sees your _____ .

5. lot   let

Do not _____ the fox get it!

6. legs   lags

The fox jogs fast on its _____ .

7. Tin   Then

_____ it finds its den.

8. happen   hectic

What will _____ here?

9. bad   bed

The fox naps in its _____ !

Handwriting

High Frequency Words

Trace each High Frequency Word and then write it.

down down

or or

their their

they they

with with

them them

your your

be be

● Word Cards: Words with short *e*

jet	hen	helmet	bell
vet	nest	bet	beg
sell	men	peg	pet
tell	best	forget	set
red	help	bell	lend
rest	yell	den	send
ten	fell	test	end

High Frequency Word Cards

am	as
him	with
for	their
at	be
go	them
to	your
we	down
has	they
she	or

Name _____   Date _____

Short *u*

Circle the word that names the picture.

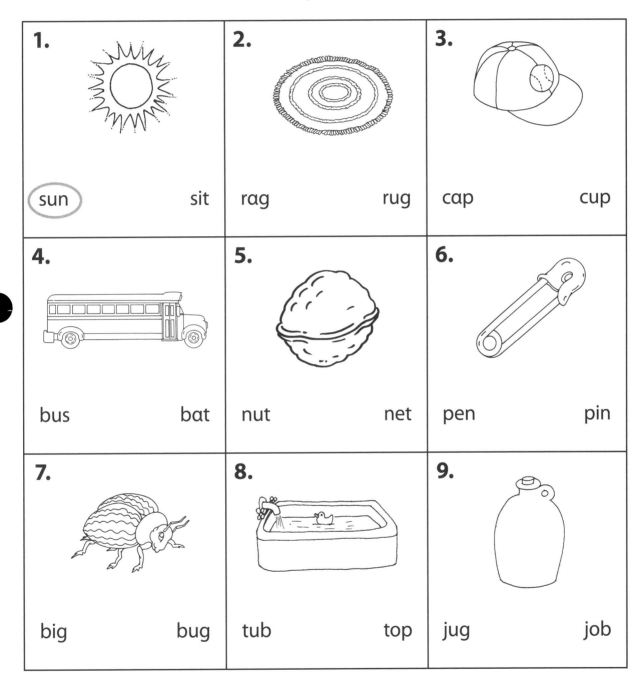

1. (sun) sit	**2.** rag rug	**3.** cap cup
4. bus bat	**5.** nut net	**6.** pen pin
7. big bug	**8.** tub top	**9.** jug job

Read It Together   What bugs do you like?

Name _____ Date _____

Kittens in a Basket

Write a word from the box to complete each sentence.

_____

1. What is in _____ basket?

High Frequency **Words**
be
down
or
their
them
they
with
your

2. I have kittens. Look down, and you can

_____

see _____ .

_____

3. Look at _____ legs.

They look like mittens!

_____

4. It can _____ fun to have a kitten. Can I

get one?

_____

5. You can have the big kitten _____ the

little one.

_____

6. You can have fun _____ your kitten.

Name _____ Date _____

Use Proper Nouns

1. Take turns with a partner.

2. Toss a marker onto the game board.

3. Follow the directions in the square you land on.

Say a sentence with a **day of the week**.	Say a sentence with a **month**.	Say a sentence with a **holiday**.
Say a sentence with a **day of the week**.	Say a sentence with a **proper noun that names a special date**.	Say a sentence with a **holiday**.
Say a sentence with **two different days of the week**.	Say a sentence with **two different months**.	Say a sentence with **two different holidays**.

Phonics

Short *u*

Write the word that completes each sentence.

1. up   an

The sun comes _____ , and Gus gets out of bed.

2. mud   muffin

He gets a _____ . Yum!

3. nets   nuts

It has _____ in it. Yum! Yum!

4. jogs   jugs

Gus _____ with his pal Jed.

5. us   until

They run _____ ten.

6. hut   hot

Then the sun gets too _____ .

7. fun   fan

The pals get wet and have _____ .

8. sat   sunset

Gus sees the sun go down. He likes the _____ .

9. bed   bud

Gus is in his _____ . He had a fun day!

● **Grammar and Writing**

Write Proper Nouns

Read the story. Then choose a word from the box that goes with each sentence.

September	Fourth of July	Peterson Fireworks Company
Mrs. Minh	Oak Street	Saturday

Brandon was walking down _Oak Street_____. it was

● a sunny _____ morning in _____. Up on

the next block he saw lots of flashing lights. *Hmm*, he

thought, *it looks like the fireworks on the* _____.

Brandon crossed the street and walked up to the next

block. There he saw a bunch of fire engines and police

cars. He saw his neighbor _____ looking at a

building. She waved to Brandon and then pointed at

_____. The building was on fire! *It*

● *really is like Independence Day*, thought Brandon.

Vocabulary

Vocabulary Bingo

1. **Write one Key Word in each building.**

2. **Listen to the clues. Find the Key Word and use a marker to cover it.**

3. **Say "Bingo" when you have four markers in a row.**

Key Words	
area	locate
building	park
home	place
hospital	population
identify	school
library	

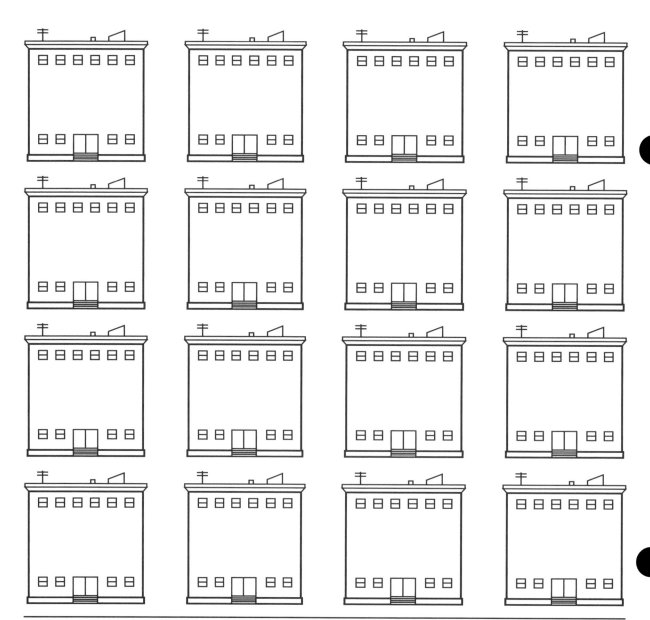

For use with TE p. T51g

PM1.39

Name _____   Date _____

●

Be My Neighbor

Make a details cluster for "Be My Neighbor." Look for details that tell more about the main idea.

●

● **Tell a partner about the main idea and details in "Be My Neighbor."**

Phonics

Consonants *ck, ng*

Circle the word that names the picture.

1. dug / (duck) / dud	**2.** song / sob / sock	**3.** lick / lock / long
4. rabbit / rocket / robs	**5.** lock / lots / long	**6.** sit / sick / sing
7. tang / tag / tack	**8.** jack / jacket / jam	**9.** king / kin / kitten
10. kick / kit / kiss	**11.** wick / wing / wins	**12.** rang / rock / rots

Read It Together The king with a ring can sing!

Name _____ Date _____

Consonants *ck, ng*

Write the word that completes each sentence.

1. **King   Kick**

   _____ Nick is sad.

2. **ring   rips**

   He cannot find his red _____ .

3. **jogs   jacket**

   He finds his red _____ .

4. **people   pocket**

   He looks in the _____ .

5. **song   sock**

   He finds a tan _____ with zigzags.

6. **pack   pang**

   He finds a _____ of gum, too.

7. **dug   duck**

   Then Nick sees his pet _____ .

8. **wing   wick**

   The duck has Nick's ring on his _____ .

9. **lock   long**

   Nick is not sad! He sings a _____ song!

Phonics

Double Consonants

Write the word to complete each sentence.

1. hiss   hill

Jack and Jill go up a _____ .

2. pass   pack

They _____ a big log.

3. mock   moss

It has _____ on it.

4. eggs   adds

The pals sit down to have some _____ .

5. mill   mess

They make a _____ .

6. buzz   buck

Some bugs come out and _____ by.

7. ill   off

Jack and Jill hop _____ that log!

8. will   wing

What _____ they do?

9. huff   hull   putt   puff

They _____ and _____ and run back down!

Name _____ Date _____

High Frequency Words

Trace each High Frequency Word and then write it.

each each

no no

said said

saw saw

use use

was was

were were

● Word Cards: Words with *-ck, -ng*

sock	truck	string	building
black	duck	hung	trick
tackle	ring	fling	quick
hang	bang	slick	tickle
sing	thing	strong	rung
lock	flock	rock	song
lick	sung	long	nick

For use with TE p. T53g   **PM1.45**   Unit 1 | Hello, Neighbor!

●High Frequency Word Cards

like	when
but	said
so	no
this	use
if	was
that	were
he	saw
in	each
up	who

Name _____ Date _____

Comparison Chart

Compare Media

Use this chart to compare "Be My Neighbor" and "My Favorite Place."

	Photo-Essay	Internet Bulletin Board
has photos	✓	✓
has captions		
has more than one writer		
gives facts		
asks and answers questions		
lets people share ideas and communicate		

 Take turns with a partner. Ask each other questions about a photo-essay or an Internet bulletin board.

Name _____ Date _____

Phonics
Short Vowels

Circle the word that names the picture.

1. cot / (cat) / cut	**2.** lock / lick / luck	**3.** nut / not / net
4. socks / sax / six	**5.** bus / bass / boss	**6.** rung / rang / ring
7. hit / hat / hut	**8.** mat / mitt / mutt	**9.** ten / tan / tin
10. bud / bad / bed	**11.** cup / cap / cop	**12.** leg / log / lag

Read It Together   I see six socks and a sax!

PM1.48   **Unit 1** | Hello, Neighbor!

What Did We See?

Write a word from the box to complete each sentence.

High Frequency **Words**
each
no
said
saw
use
was
where
who

1. Matt said, "Can you tell what my pals

   _____

   _____ pass by?".

2. Ming said, "They _____ little."

3. Mack said, "Was _____ one tan?"

4. Pam said, "_____. One was tan."

5. Lin said, "They _____ their legs to hop."

6. Matt said, "What did my pals see? _____

   can tell us?"

●Word Cards

	,	s	
house	street	neighborhood	friends
Mom	Dad	Grandmother	Grandfather
dogs	birds	trees	leaves
cars	trucks	sidewalk	park
ponds	bugs	zoo	animals
buildings	bus	trains	schools
playground	stores	bridge	Mr. Flores
Mrs. Brown	Dr. Adams	Capt. Smith	policewoman

Name _____ Date _____

Short Vowels

Write the words to complete each sentence.

1. big   fills

Sid _____ his _____ basket with eggs.

2. pal   runs

Then Sid _____ to find his _____ Ross.

3. ten   has

Sid _____ _____ eggs for Ross.

4. did   get

Where _____ Sid _____ the eggs for Ross?

5. pet   got

He _____ them from his _____ hens!

6. sells   but

Sid _____ some of his eggs, _____ not all of them.

7. packs   not

He _____ up the eggs that he did _____ sell.

8. pan   mix

His mom can _____ them up in a _____ .

9. picnic   will

Sid _____ have them at his _____ . Yum!

Name _____ Date _____

Write Possessive Nouns and Abbreviations

Read the story. Then choose a word from the box that goes with each sentence.

Mr.	Jason's	Ling's
sister's	puppies'	neighbors'

I really like my neighborhood. Some of my

neighbors' homes are big and some are small. My

friend _____ house is across the street. It's big

because he has eight brothers and sisters. My

_____ boyfriend lives in a little house on the next

block. He plays soccer with me sometimes. _____

Ling lives next door. I like to play with Mrs. _____

new puppies in their back yard. The _____ fur is

very soft, but their tongues are rough!

Grammar: Proper and Possessive Nouns

Use Proper and Possessive Nouns

Grammar Rules Proper and Possessive Nouns

- A proper noun names a specific person, place, or thing. (Example: Texas)

- Some titles of people begin with a capital letter and end with a period. (Example: Dr.)

- A possessive noun names an owner. (Example: Jackson's)

Underline the proper nouns and write them in the chart. Then make each proper noun possessive. The first one is done for you.

<u>Mrs. Preston</u> lives in a neighborhood called Grandview. Her home is on Maple Street. Adam Preston is her son. We go to the same school. He is on my soccer team, too. Mr. Mohr is our coach.

Proper Nouns	Proper Possessive Nouns
Mrs. Preston	Mrs. Preston's

 Write a sentence with a proper noun and a proper possessive noun. Read your sentence to a partner.

Name _____ Date _____

Blends with r, l

Circle the word that names the picture.

1. tag / (flag) / drag	**2.** plug / slug / jug	**3.** class / glass / grass
4. drum / plum / hum	**5.** log / clog / frog	**6.** truck / cluck / pluck
7. flap / trap / clap	**8.** bricks / tricks / flicks	**9.** slab / crab / lab
10. frock / block / clock	**11.** grin / win / bring	**12.** drill / flannel / pretzel

Read It Together   Grin and clap if you like pretzels.

Name _____ Date _____

The Nature Walk

Make a story map to tell about a nature walk.

> **Beginning:**
> How does the story start?

↓

> **Middle:**
> What happens next in the story?

↓

> **End:**
> How does the story end?

 Share your Beginning-Middle-End Chart with your partner.

Name _____ Date _____

Blends with *r, l*

Write the word that completes each sentence.

1. plus   drums

Tran's dad has _____.

2. bless   brass

Some of them are _____.

3. trumpet   trot

Tran has a _____.

4. click   plastic

It is not _____. It is brass!

5. bran   plan

Dad and Tran have a _____.

6. truck   pluck

Tran and Dad get into the red _____.

7. bring   cling

They _____ their drums and trumpet.

8. glass   class

Then they go to Tran's _____.

9. trap   clap

All of Tran's pals _____.

Name _____ Date _____

● **Handwriting**

High Frequency Words

Trace each High Frequency Word and then write it.

these these

body body

back back

● how how

eat eat

those those

way way

● into into

●Word Cards: Blends with *r, l*

flag	brick	clock	truck
flatten	plastic	trick	problem
black	grip	block	trap
dragon	frantic	click	slap
traffic	grass	slid	glad
crab	plan	printed	glob
blast	drop	slip	cracking

For use with TE p. T65k   **PM2.5**   Unit 2 | Staying Alive

● High Frequency Word Cards

what	way
help	back
people	eat
do	those
there	how
by	into
day	these
then	body

Name _____ Date _____

Phonics

Blends with *s*

Circle the word that names the picture.

1. stop / flop / snap	**2.** sting / scan / spin	**3.** trim / skim / swim
4. sped / sled / skid	**5.** spell / smell / swell	**6.** spill / still / frill
7. fling / sling / swing	**8.** stack / snack / scuff	**9.** steps / snaps / snips
10. skip / slip / clip	**11.** stock / slot / spot	**12.** slim / stem / skin

Read It Together Do you like to swim, skip, or swing?

Name _____ Date _____

A Pack of Pretzels

Write a word from the box to complete each sentence.

High Frequency **Words**
back
body
eat
how
into
these
those
way

1. Fran said, "What is in that pack on the

_____ of your body?"

2. Fred said, "Look. I have a lot of stuff to _____ in it."

3. Fran said, "These are nuts. Are _____ pretzels?"

4. Fred said, "Yes. I like to snack on pretzels." _____
do you like them?

5. Fran bit _____ a pretzel.

6. Fran said, "I like them a lot! I will find a _____ to
get pretzels, too!"

Name _____ Date _____

Build Sentences

Cut out the cards and make a gray pile with the cards facedown. Spread out the white cards face up. Pick one gray card. Then choose a white card that matches the gray card you picked. Say a sentence using the word on the gray card and the word on the white card. Then put the cards on the bottom of the piles.

can	might	do	does
fly	eat	think	run
hold	wish	drink	play
hear	see	taste	listen
walk	swim	imagine	touch

For use with TE p. T65n   **PM2.9**   Unit 2 | Staying Alive

Phonics

Blends with *s*

Write the word that completes each sentence.

1. stiff   sniff

The dogs _____ in the grass.

2. stick   slick

One dog finds a _____ in the grass.

3. slot   spot

One dog finds a _____ in the sun and naps.

4. smell   swell

One dog sniffs. What can it _____?

5. slug   snug

It smells a fox that is _____ in its den.

6. slop   stop

Then the fox runs and will not _____.

7. still   squid

The dog is _____, but looks at the fox.

8. spill   speck

The fox runs until it is a little _____.

9. scans   stacks

The dog _____ the grass. It cannot see the fox.

Name _____   Date _____

Triple Blends with *s*

Circle the word that names the picture.

1. spot / stick / (split)	**2.** scraps / stacks / skips	**3.** sting / spring / sling
4. swing / string / sprig	**5.** scrub / stub / scab	**6.** splat / slat / scat
7. scram / slum / strum	**8.** snap / sap / strap	**9.** sprig / swig / strung
10. sprung / strong / scrod	**11.** sprang / stuck / struck	**12.** scruff / stuff / snuff

Read It Together   The strong dog springs up, eats scraps, and scrams!

For use with TE p. T88b   **PM2.11**   **Unit 2** | Staying Alive

Grammar and Writing

Write Action and Helping Verbs

Read the story. Then choose a word from the box that goes with each sentence.

carries	can fly	might sit
spot	sees	peep

An owl _____*can fly*_____ without making any

noise. This bird also _____ very well in the

dark. A hunting owl _____ on a tree branch

to look and listen for small animals. Hungry baby

owls _____ impatiently for food. After

catching its dinner, the owl _____ it back to

its nest. If you _____ an owl, you have been

very lucky!

Name _____ Date _____

Twilight Hunt

Make a Beginning-Middle-End Chart to show the plot of "Twilight Hunt."

> **Beginning:**
> Screech Owl goes on a hunt. She must find food for her babies.

⬇

> **Middle:**

⬇

> **End:**

 Use your Beginning-Middle-End Chart to tell your partner about "Twilight Hunt."

Name _____ Date _____

Final Blends

Circle the word that names the picture.

1. plot / (plant) / plan	2. hand / hack / hang	3. skin / skit / skunk
4. nest / net / neck	5. best / bent / belt	6. lamp / land / lack
7. rang / raft / ramp	8. deck / dent / desk	9. test / tent / tell
10. bank / bang / band	11. vent / vend / vest	12. stamp / stack / stand

Read It Together Do you camp in a desk, a bank, or a tent?

Phonics

Final Blends

Write the word that completes each sentence.

1. pot   pond

Trent just got to the _____.

2. jump   just

He will sprint down, _____ in, and get wet!

3. pant   past

Trent swims _____ plants and frogs.

4. drink   drift

Then Trent comes out and gets a _____.

5. gulp   gust

He likes to _____ it down fast.

6. sand   sang

Trent digs in the _____ for the rest of the day.

7. song   soft

The sand is _____ when it is wet.

8. cast   camp

Trent, his mom, and his dad _____ at the pond.

9. tent   test

At the end of the day, they go into their _____.

● **Handwriting**

High Frequency Words

Trace each High Frequency Word and then write it.

could could

good good

hard hard

● now now

over over

part part

under under

●very very

● Word Cards: Final Blends

plant	jump	hand	trunk
hunt	must	slant	fond
wind	insect	trust	connect
help	blend	blank	plump
bank	think	lost	stamp
drink	subtract	gulp	clamp
stand	pink	stunt	fact

●High Frequency Word Cards

of	now
out	over
one	under
some	very
from	could
come	good
her	part
look	hard

Name _____   Date _____

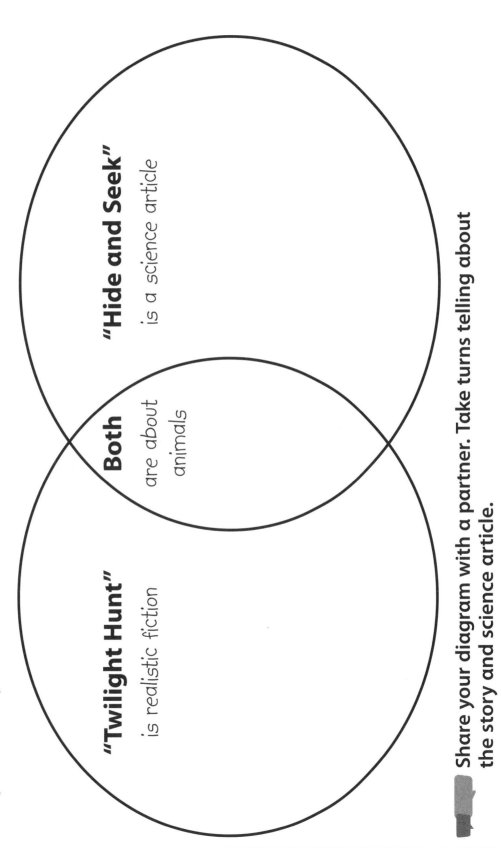

Venn Diagram

Compare Genres

Compare a story and a science article.

"Hide and Seek"
is a science article

Both
are about animals

"Twilight Hunt"
is realistic fiction

Share your diagram with a partner. Take turns telling about the story and science article.

For use with TE p. T97g

PM2.19

Phonics

Syllable Division

Circle the word that names the picture. Divide the word into syllables.

1. basket / bobsled / (backpack)	**2.** drumsticks / ducklings / dentists	**3.** pumpkin / public / puppet
4. witness / windmill / wisdom	**5.** mattress / mistrust / manhunt	**6.** handbag / happen / napkin
7. hiccup / himself / hilltop	**8.** 100 husband / helmet / hundred	**9.** sandbox / sapling / sadness
10. actress / anthill / attack	**11.** address / album / attract	**12.** 10 − 7 subset / subject / subtract

Read It Together   We saw hundreds of anthills on the hilltop.

PM2.20

Unit 2 | Staying Alive

Name _____ Date _____

Find the Backpack!

Write a word from the box to complete each sentence.

High Frequency **Words**
could
good
hard
now
over
part
under
very

● **1.** Where _____ my backpack be?

2. It is _____ hard to find! Can you help me?

3. It is not _____ my bed or over my bed.

4. It is not on my desk! Where can I look _____?

5. Look at my jacket! I see a strap under it! Is the strap

_____ of my backpack?

● **6.** It is _____ that I have my backpack. Now where
are my mittens?

Grammar: Helping Verbs

Use Helping Verbs

Directions:

1. Make a spinner.

2. Play with a partner.

3. Take turns spinning the spinner.

4. Read the word you land on. Say a sentence using **can**, **might**, **do**, or **does**. Then have your partner say another sentence using the same helping verb and a different main verb.

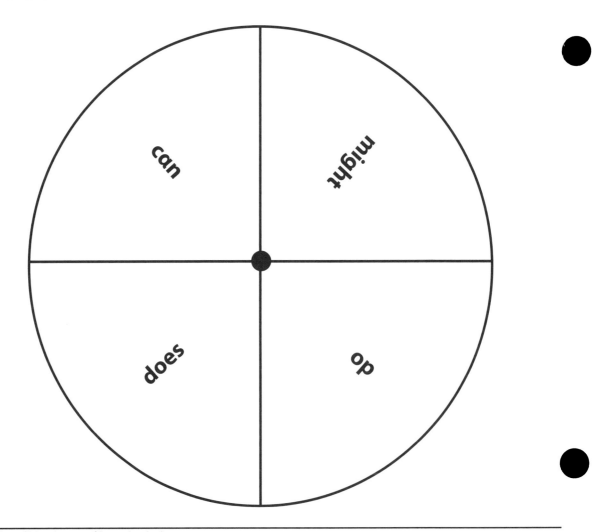

Make a Spinner

1. Put a paper clip ⬭ in the center of the circle.

2. Hold one end of the paper clip with a pencil.

3. Spin the paper clip around the pencil.

Name _____ Date _____

Syllable Division

Divide the words into syllables. Then write the word that completes each sentence.

1. hilltop   tantrum

Bess and Kent jog up to the _____.

2. instant   anthill

What do they see? Bess sees an _____!

3. dentist   inspects

Bess looks down and _____ it.

4. address   hundreds

She sees _____ of ants.

5. ducklings   subtracts

Kent sees six _____ in a pond.

6. handful   grandpa

Then Bess and Kent see their _____.

7. backpack   tundra

He gets a snack from his _____.

8. pumpkin   napkin

The snack is _____ muffins.

9. helmets   gumdrops

They eat muffins with _____ on top!

Write Helping and Action Verbs

Read the story. Choose a word from the box that goes with each sentence.

can	do	does
hide	look	might

Some animals can __hide__ themselves to stay

safe. An insect _____ use color or shape

to hide from its enemies. A mantis really _____

depend on its green color and leaf shape to hide.

A little red fish does _____ exactly like the plants

around it! Some birds _____ blend in with the

trees and flowers around them. If I look on leaves

carefully, I _____ find a mantis or a katydid.

Name _____ Date _____

Roll a Verb

Grammar Rules Action and Helping Verbs

For Action Verbs
- Use **-s** at the end of an action verb if the subject is **he**, **she**, or **it**.
- Do not use **-s** for **I**, **you**, **we**, or **they**.

For Action Verbs with Helping Verbs
- A **helping verb** comes before the **main verb**.

Use a numbered game cube to play this game.

1. Roll the game cube. Find the helping verb that goes with the number.

2. Roll the game cube again. Find the action verb that goes with the number.

3. Say a sentence with the action verb and helping verb. The first player to use all six action verbs and helping verbs in sentences correctly wins.

Helping Verbs	Action Verbs
1. do	1. look
2. does	2. escape
3. can	3. fly
4. might	4. run
5. do	5. search
6. can	6. hide

Name _____ Date _____

Words with *ch, tch*

Circle the word that names the picture.

1. chick (circled) / brick / quick	**2.** camp / catch / cast	**3.** past / pack / patch
4. flunk / chunk / skunk	**5.** branch / hatch / brand	**6.** chin / grin / spin
7. match / mast / mask	**8.** drums / strums / chums	**9.** crank / crutch / crust
10. fleck / speck / check	**11.** sandwich / sapling / such	**12.** object / ostrich / chimp

Read It Together Chuck and his chums scratch their chins.

PM2.26 Unit 2 | Staying Alive

Name _____ Date _____

Creature Features

Compare animals and their features.

Features	Creature 1	Creature 2

Tell a partner how the animals are alike.

Name _____ Date _____

Words with *ch, tch*

Write the word that completes each sentence.

1. chipmunk   trunk

A little _____ collects nuts.

2. chunk   lunch

Will it eat the nuts for its _____?

3. children   munch

I like to _____ on nuts, too!

4. chimp   catch

A big _____ eats some nuts.

5. clump   chomp

It likes to _____ on plants, bugs, and eggs, too.

6. chat   sandwich

I eat an egg _____ for a snack!

7. ostrich   odd

An _____ eats plants, sand, and bugs.

8. switch   chicken

One of its eggs is like 24 _____ eggs. That is very big!

9. quench   champ

It runs very fast, too. The ostrich is such a _____!

Name _____ Date _____

 Handwriting

High Frequency Words

Trace each High Frequency Word and then write it.

wait wait

know know

other other

warm warm

year year

yellow yellow

world world

without without

● Word Cards: Words with *ch, tch*

chest	watch	champ	patch
itch	children	chimp	pitch
lunchbox	chatting	batch	check
chill	catch	fetch	stretch
chin	switch	attach	chick
scratch	kitchen	stitch	hatch
rich	bench	ditch	inch

● High Frequency Word Cards

with	other
their	know
be	year
them	without
your	wait
down	warm
they	world
or	yellow

Name _____ Date _____

Words with *th, wh*

Circle the word that names the picture.

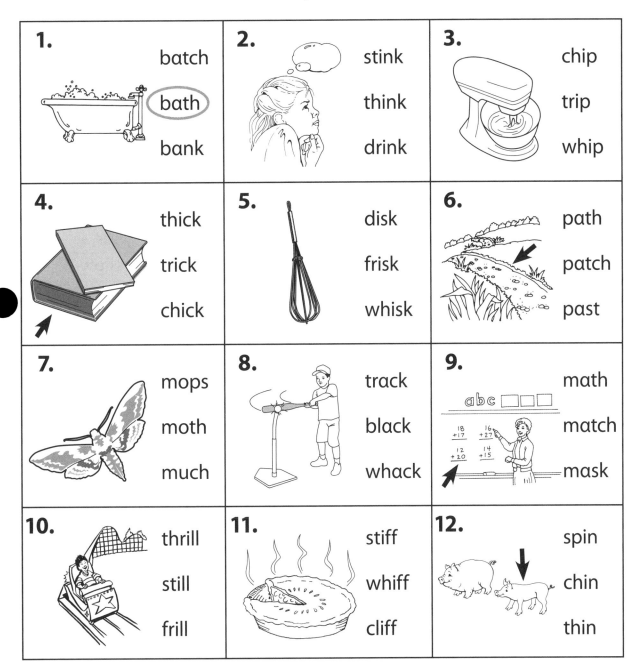

1.
- batch
- (bath)
- bank

2.
- stink
- think
- drink

3.
- chip
- trip
- whip

4.
- thick
- trick
- chick

5.
- disk
- frisk
- whisk

6.
- path
- patch
- past

7.
- mops
- moth
- much

8.
- track
- black
- whack

9.
- math
- match
- mask

10.
- thrill
- still
- frill

11.
- stiff
- whiff
- cliff

12.
- spin
- chin
- thin

Read It Together What do you think? Is a moth thick or thin?

For use with TE p. T105c   **PM2.32**   Unit 2 | Staying Alive

What Is It?

Write a word from the box to complete each sentence.

High Frequency Words
know
other
wait
warm
without
world
year
yellow

1. Each year, people all over the _____ see it. No one is without it.

2. I am _____ when I sit in it.

3. It looks _____ in the day and red when it sets.

4. I saw it set the _____ day.

5. If you _____ here, you can see it set, too.

6. Do you _____ what it is? It is the sun!

● **Grammar: Use Has, Have, Had**

Sentences: Has, Have, Had

Cut cards. Spread both the gray cards and the white cards face up.
Choose one of each and say a sentence using those two words.

has	have	had
I	you	he	she
it	we	they	cat
dog	horse	bird	fish
wings	tail	fur	feathers
scales	animals	pets	lions
teeth	friends	neighbors	parents

Phonics

Words with *th, wh*

Write the word that completes each sentence.

1. sixth   whiff

What is that smell? Did you get a _____ of it?

2. think   wink

I _____ Dad is in the kitchen!

3. bring   broth

That smell must be his chicken _____.

4. thing   string

It is the best _____ to eat for lunch.

5. thick   chick

It is not _____. It is thin.

6. then   when

I eat it _____ it is still warm!

7. which   stitch

There are buns and muffins, too. Dad asks _____ I want.

8. wink   with

I will have a bun _____ my broth.

9. thank   whisk

Then I _____ Dad for a very good lunch!

Phonics

Contractions

she + is = she's
can + not = can't

Write the contraction for the two underlined words on the line.

1. You can see that <u>he</u> <u>is</u> sick.

You can see that _____ sick.

2. You can see that <u>she</u> <u>is</u> not sick.

You can see that _____ not sick.

3. Do you think <u>it</u> <u>is</u> fun to be sick?

Do you think _____ fun to be sick?

4. You <u>can</u> <u>not</u> be with your pals.

You _____ be with your pals.

5. You <u>do</u> <u>not</u> have much fun.

You _____ have much fun.

Phonics

Contractions

I + am = I'm
you + are = you're

Write the contraction for the two underlined words on the line.

1. I am in the pond.

_____ in the pond.

2. You are in the pond, too.

_____ in the pond, too.

3. We are all wet!

_____ all wet!

4. My dog can not swim.

My dog _____ swim.

5. We do not let my dog jump into the pond!

We _____ let my dog jump into the pond!

Grammar and Writing

Write Irregular Verbs

Read the letter. Then choose a word from the box that goes with each sentence.

were	have	had
has	was	is

Dear Brandon,

I am having a great time at sea camp. This

camp ___has___ lots of cool things to do.

The water in the ocean _____ warm and

clear. That means it is easy to see fish. Yesterday, I

_____ fun on a boat. It _____ exciting to zoom

through the waves. Seagulls and other birds _____

all around the boat. I will come home Saturday. I

_____ a special surprise from sea camp for you!

Your friend,

Ali

Name _____ Date _____

Living Lights

Make a chart to compare bioluminescent animals.

How It Uses Light	Animal
to attract prey	glowworm anglerfish
to send messages	
to hide	

 Use your comparison chart to tell a partner about the animals in "Living Lights."

Name _____   Date _____

Words with *sh, ph*

Circle the word that names the picture.

1. smell / fell / (shell)	**2.** dish / ding / ditch	**3.** shed / bled / sped
4. grass / graph / grand	**5.** stop / chop / shop	**6.** fish / fill / fist
7. whip / chip / ship	**8.** mask / mash / match	**9.** brunch / brush / brick
10. split / splash / scratch	**11.** shrub / scrub / stub	**12.** tramp / track / trash

Read It Together   She sells fish and shells at her shop.

PM2.40

Phonics

Words with *sh, ph*

Write the word that completes each sentence.

1. **graph   shellfish**

   We can see _____ in this tank.

2. **shells   fresh**

   They have no fins. They have _____.

3. **shrimp   squish**

   This tank has _____ in it.

4. **swish   dolphins**

   Over here are the _____.

5. **shock   fish**

   They swim, but they are not _____.

6. **mammals   shrunk**

   They are _____ like you and me!

7. **shack   splash**

   Look out! They will _____ and get you wet!

8. **dash   damp**

   Now we _____ over to see the man in the tank.

9. **shelf   wish**

   I _____ I could swim in the tank with him!

Handwriting

High Frequency Words

Trace each High Frequency Word and then write it.

call call

more more

than than

two two

walk walk

why why

young young

because because

Word Cards: Words with *sh, ph*

fish	shell	dolphin	phlox
wish	graph	splash	phone
bush	phase	push	phrase
dash	phonics	wash	orphan
shift	elephant	she	trophy
shelf	shut	alphabet	shrug
Phil	ashen	photo	shop

●High Frequency Word Cards

other	call
know	more
year	two
● without	walk
wait	than
warm	young
world	why
● yellow	because

Name _____ Date _____

Compare Genres

Use a comparison chart to compare "Living Lights" and "Clever Creatures."

Features	"Living Lights"	"Clever Creatures"
is about animals	✓	✓
includes words that rhyme		✓
has facts		
has photographs		
has illustrations		

 Work with a partner. Read each feature and see if it is in "Living Lights" and "Clever Creatures." Make a check if you see the feature.

●Words with *-ed, -ing*

Find the match for your card. Act it out.

jump	kick
blink	stretch
● jumped	jumping
kicked	kicking
blinked	blinking
● stretched	stretching

Name _____ Date _____

Walking the Dog

Write a word from the box to complete each sentence.

High Frequency **Words**
because
call
more
than
two
walk
why
young

1. I have a _____ dog. My dog is still a pup.

2. I _____ with my pup each day.

3. On some days, we go on _____ than one walk.

4. We go on _____ walks.

5. I call my pup to me now. _____ do I call her?

6. I call her _____ we are going on a walk!

Name _____ Date _____

Use Contractions of *Be* and *Have*

Directions:

1. Take turns with a partner.

2. Toss a marker onto the game board.

3. Follow the directions in the square your marker lands on.

4. After you say your sentence, your partner follows these steps:

   • Say your partner's sentence with a contraction.

   • Say your partner's sentence with a contraction and *not*.

   • If your partner's sentence is singular, make it plural. If your partner's sentence is plural, make it singular.

Say a sentence with <u>am</u>.	Say a sentence with <u>is</u>.
Say a sentence with <u>are</u>.	Say a sentence with <u>has</u>.
Say a sentence with <u>have</u>.	Say a sentence with <u>had</u>.

Phonics

Words with *-ed, -ing*

Write the word with *-ed* or *-ing* to complete each sentence.

1. go

Gramps and Ben are _____ fishing.

2. want

Last year, Ben _____ to go, but he was too young.

3. pack

Ben just _____ all his fishing stuff.

4. help

Gramps _____ him.

5. stand

Now Gramps and Ben are _____ on the dock.

6. splash

The fish are _____.

7. pass

One big fish just _____ by them!

8. hand

Ben is _____ Gramps his fishing rod.

9. look

He is _____ at the fish. That is more fun than catching them!

Phonics

Plurals -s, -es

Write the word with -s or -es to complete each sentence.

1. **thing**

   What _____ will we see if we walk down this path?

2. **fox**

   Look over there! I see two _____ in the grass.

3. **branch**

   What is up in those _____?

4. **nest**

   I see two _____.

5. **egg**

   There are little _____ in them.

6. **shrub**

   Do you see those _____ by the pond?

7. **skunk**

   Some _____ are under them.

8. **bench**

   We can sit on the _____ over there.

9. **sandwich**

   Then we can eat _____ for lunch.

Grammar and Writing

Write Full Forms of *Be* and *Have*

Read the report. Then choose words from the box that go with each sentence.

has not	they are	she had
I am	I have	is not

My name is Bella and ___I am___ interested in animals, especially insects. I think _____ very interesting. Did you know that not all bugs are insects? Insects have six legs. A spider _____ an insect because it has eight legs. I love to read books about insects. _____ just finished one about insects that change color. I loaned it to my sister Alex, but she _____ finished it yet. She said _____ already started another book, so my bug book would just have to wait!

Name _____ Date _____

Insects at the Zoo

Grammar Rules Verbs *be* and *have*

Verbs should match who or what they are telling about.

For yourself, use	**am**	I **am** a scientist.
	have	I **have** work to do.
For one other person or thing, use	**is**	The Io moth **is** very clever.
	has	It **has** wings that look like big eyes.
For one other person, yourself and others, or other people and things, use	**are**	These wings **are** a clever trick.
	have	Many moths **have** features that keep them safe.

Choose the correct verb. Then read the sentence to a partner.

1. My teacher ____*is*____ interested in all kinds of insects.
is / are

2. He _____ good news for our class.
has / have

3. We _____ on our way to the zoo on Friday!
is / are

4. The zoo _____ a special place to see insects.
has / have

5. I _____ excited about the trip to the zoo.
am / is

6. You _____ invited to come, too!
is / are

Name _____   Date _____

Words with Long *a*

Circle the word that goes with each picture.

1. gap gum (game)	**2.** rake rack rock	**3.** cane can cap
4. tape tip tap	**5.** cap cape cup	**6.** lack lake lock
7. pluck plate pat	**8.** whale well whack	**9.** snack snake snap
10. brag brake brick	**11.** pan plan plane	**12.** man mane mast

Read It Together   Do you see waves or rakes in the lake?

Name _____ Date _____

Problem and Solution

Fill out a problem-and-solution chart.

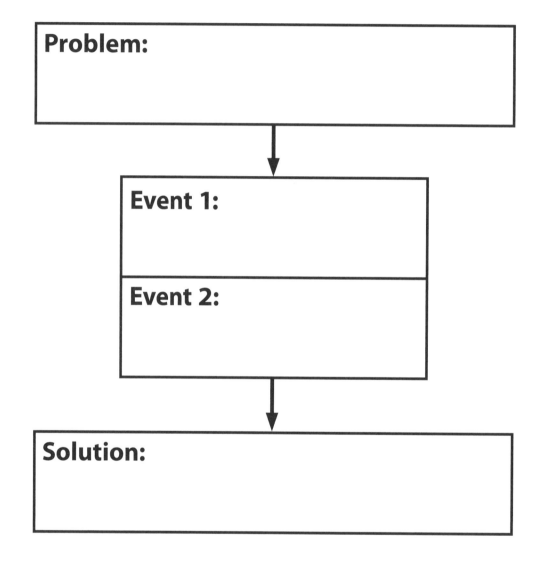

Problem:

Event 1:

Event 2:

Solution:

Tell a partner about a problem you solved.

Grammar: Adjectives

Adjectives and Nouns

Find an adjective and a noun that rhyme from the word banks.
Write the rhyming pair next to the riddle it answers.

Adjectives		
dry	wet	gray
dark	swell	loud
nice	damp	

Nouns		
cloud	ice	sky
camp	park	pet
day	well	

1. What is a soaked puppy called? a _wet pet_

2. What is smooth, frozen water called? _____

3. What is a big tent after a rainfall called? a _____

4. What is a rainy Monday called? a _____

5. What is a playground during a strong storm called? a _____

6. What is a lack of clouds called? a _____

7. What is rumbling thunder called? a _____

8. What is a great place to get water called? a _____

Name _____ Date _____

Phonics

Words with Long *a*

Write the word that completes each sentence.

1. wade   cake

Zane and Jake _____ into the lake.

2. tack   take

They _____ a quick dip and swim to the raft.

3. tapes   waves

Then Mom _____ at them, and they swim back.

4. cave   make

Zane finds a _____ in some rocks.

5. bats   bakes

What is in it? Are there _____ and snakes?

6. manes   chases

Jake _____ Zane back to Mom and Dad.

7. snack   snake

They _____ on sandwiches.

8. states   grapes

Then they eat a bunch of _____ .

9. trade   late

It gets _____ . They pack up and go back to their van.

Handwriting

High Frequency Words

Trace each High Frequency Word and then write it.

cold cold

form form

turn turn

drink drink

live live

water water

feel feel

three three

●Word Cards: Long *a*

lake	game	tape	plate
date	shake	flake	came
shape	drape	state	snake
flame	wake	name	gate
late	same	take	frame
cape	crate	scrape	brake
skate	quake	blame	grape

● High Frequency Word Cards

back	cold
how	drink
those	feel
● body	form
into	live
way	three
eat	turn
● these	water

● **Phonics**

Syllables

Circle the word that goes with each picture.

1. channel / (chase) / champs	**2.** panes / pancakes / pandas	**3.** scallop / scab / skate
4. cascade / cape / cupcake	**5.** frame / frank / frantic	**6.** vase / invade / vane
7. upstate / unmade / upset	**8.** exam / exit / exhale	**9.** snack / snake / snap
10. unsafe / unlace / subtract	**11.** end / escape / engrave	**12.** $\begin{array}{r} 2 \\ +\ 2 \\ \hline 3 \end{array}$ make / mistrust / mistake

● **Read It Together**   Do you like cupcakes or pancakes?

High Frequency Words

At the Lake

Write a word from the box to complete each sentence.

High Frequency Words
cold
drink
feel
form
live
three
turn
water

1. Jane swims in the _____ at the lake.

2. It feels very _____ .

3. Fish live in the lake. Jane sees _____ swim by.

4. Then they _____ back and swim by Jane.

5. Jane gets out of the lake and has a _____ of water.

6. This _____ of water is good to drink!

Name _____ Date _____

 Phonics

Syllables

Divide each word into syllables. Then write the word that completes each sentence.

1. invade   nickname

I am Jackson, but my _____ is Jack.

2. shameful   escape

Mom smiles and says the things I do are _____ .

3. unmade   exhale

She does not like it when my bed is _____ !

4. translate   mistake

I made a big _____ when I let the dog escape!

5. inhales   pancakes

Then there was the big mess when I made _____ !

6. unsafe   inflate

I spilled milk, and she said the mess was _____ .

7. cupcakes   inflates

But Mom has a big hug and _____ for me. Yum!

Grammar and Writing

Write Adjectives

Adjectives That Describe		Adjectives That Compare		Adjectives That Signal	
fresh	a lot	faster	fastest	this	that
huge	bright	bigger	biggest	these	those
yellow	three	softer	softest		

Read the adjectives on the chart. Choose adjectives to complete the sentences.

1. Rain did not fall for _____*three*_____ weeks.

2. The sun was _____ and hot.

3. We want to catch rain in pails by _____ porch.

4. The round pail is _____ than the square pail.

5. A _____ cloud forms in the dark sky.

6. Rain! _____ water from that cloud fills our pails.

Name _____ Date _____

Vocabulary Bingo

1. **Write one Key Word in each cloud.**

2. **Listen to the clues. Find the Key Word and use a marker to cover it.**

3. **Say "Bingo" when you have four markers in a row.**

Name _____ Date _____

Frog Brings Rain

Use a problem-and-solution chart to tell about "Frog Brings Rain."

Problem: First Woman needs Water to put out Fire.

↓

Event 1: She asks Hunting People to take Water to Fire.

↓

Event 2:

↓

Solution:

 Use your chart to tell a partner how First Woman and Frog solve the problem.

● **Phonics**

Words with Long *i*

Circle the word that names the picture.

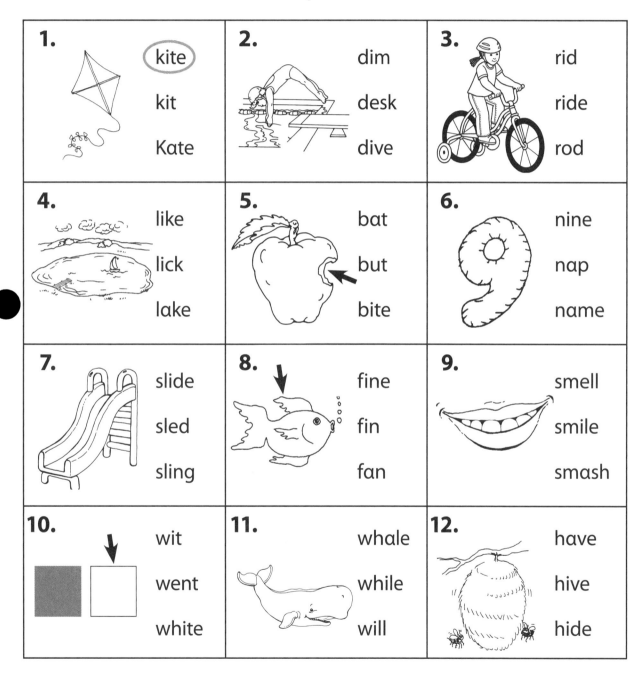

1. (kite) kit Kate	**2.** dim desk dive	**3.** rid ride rod
4. like lick lake	**5.** bat but bite	**6.** nine nap name
7. slide sled sling	**8.** fine fin fan	**9.** smell smile smash
10. wit went white	**11.** whale while will	**12.** have hive hide

● **Read It Together**   Do you like to use a kite, a bike, or a slide?

Phonics

Words with Long *i*

Write the word that completes each sentence.

1. life   beside

Mike and his dad sit _____ their tent.

2. dine   wide

They _____ on fish, rice, and grapes.

3. size   while

Mike sees a snake _____ they eat.

4. bite   sunshine

The snake does not _____ Mike.

5. hides   miles

It _____ in some rocks.

6. lines   describes

Mike _____ the snake to his dad.

7. rise   reptile

Dad tells Mike that a snake is a _____.

8. bedtime   prize

Now it is late. It is _____.

9. five   inside

Mike and Dad rest _____ their tent.

High Frequency Words

Trace each High Frequency Word and then write it.

after after

away away

before before

carry carry

does does

give give

put put

through through

● Word Cards: Long *i*, Short *i*

pine	prize	hit	rip
strike	insist	outside	glide
combine	sit	hide	pride
hid	dip	quip	side
wipe	like	whine	shine
pick	strict	trick	lip
mitten	napkin	drip	brick

● High Frequency Word Cards

now	put
over	give
under	does
very	away
could	before
good	after
part	through
hard	carry

Name _____ Date _____

Compare Explanations

Show how the two explanations for rain are different.

How Is Rain Made?	
Traditional Tale Explanation	**Science Experiment Explanation**
• Frog carries water.	• Warm, wet air rises.

 Ask a partner questions about the story and the science experiment.

PM3.19

Phonics

Words with Long *o*

Circle the word that names the picture.

1. got / (go) / get	**2.** rob / ripe / rope	**3.** dime / dome / dame
4. globe / glob / glide	**5.** haze / has / hose	**6.** cone / cane / con
7. hip / hope / hop	**8.** stock / stove / stack	**9.** phone / fine / phlox
10. raze / rose / rise	**11.** male / mile / mole	**12.** not / note / no

Read It Together Do you water with a hose, a rose, or a stove?

High Frequency Words

In the Bag

Write a word from the box to complete each sentence.

High Frequency **Words**
after
away
before
carry
does
give
put
through

1. Mom and Dad _____ a bag.

2. They _____ it down and step away from it. What's inside the bag?

3. "_____ us some hints," we beg.

4. So, _____ we look, Dad does.

5. "It does not have legs, and it swims _____ water," Dad says.

6. _____ we get those hints, we know it is a fish!

Grammar: Adjectives and Articles

Mix and Match Sentences

Choose one item from each column. Say a sentence using all three parts. Then ask your partner to say the same sentence, changing one part.

A	B	C
a an the	hour river rain cloud well hole honest	ruined my plans is very deep that Dad dug is moving swiftly covers the sun passed by slowly person I know your new shoes runs by the town will stop soon has a cover on it is a long time hides the moon is big and dark holds lots of fish is good for our garden has a bucket on a rope wait by the park

Name _____ Date _____

Words with Long o

Write the word that completes each sentence.

1. throne   go

I _____ on a hike at camp.

2. tadpoles   closes

We see some _____ in the pond.

3. so   froze

They look _____ much like little fish.

4. quote   suppose

I _____ they will be frogs one day!

5. holes   explodes

Look over there! Do you see the _____ by those stones?

6. moles   trombones

Do you think they were made by _____ or snakes?

7. opposes   pinecones

We see twigs and _____ that came down in the wind.

8. broke   flagpole

Now it is time to go and sit beside the _____.

9. rotate   home

Then it will be time to get on the bus to go _____.

Write Adjectives and Articles

Read the story. Then write a word from the box to complete each sentence.

dry	hungry	wet	a	an	the	those

Brodie and his family decided to go for ___*a*___ hike.

The hike would take several hours. Brodie took _____

apple and a granola bar in his backpack. Hiking always

made him _____.

After hiking for a while, Brodie's mom looked up at

_____ sky. "Uh-oh," she said. "Look at _____ dark

clouds. We might get _____." "No way!" answered

Brodie. "My poncho will keep me _____."

Name _____   Date _____

● **Grammar and Writing**
After the Storm

Grammar Rules Adjectives and Articles	
An **adjective** can describe what a noun is like.	→ A **light** rain starts to fall. The raindrops feel **icy** and **cold**.
An **article** can tell which noun you mean.	→ <u>A</u> cloud fills up with water. Raindrops fall on <u>the</u> green hill. It is <u>an</u> amazing thing to see.

● **Add adjectives and articles.**

The storm lasted for ___three___ days. Then the _____

sun rose. It dried up the _____ grass. _____ puddles

started to disappear. Then we looked up into the _____

sky. There was _____ amazing rainbow. It looked

_____ and _____. Soon the weather was _____

and _____ again.

● **Tell a partner about weather you like. Use adjectives and articles.**

Phonics

Words with Long e

Write the letters to name each picture.

1. we	**2.** g
3. h	**4.** sh
5. y - y	**6.** P t

Read It Together   We go to get Pete's yo-yo.

Name _____ Date _____

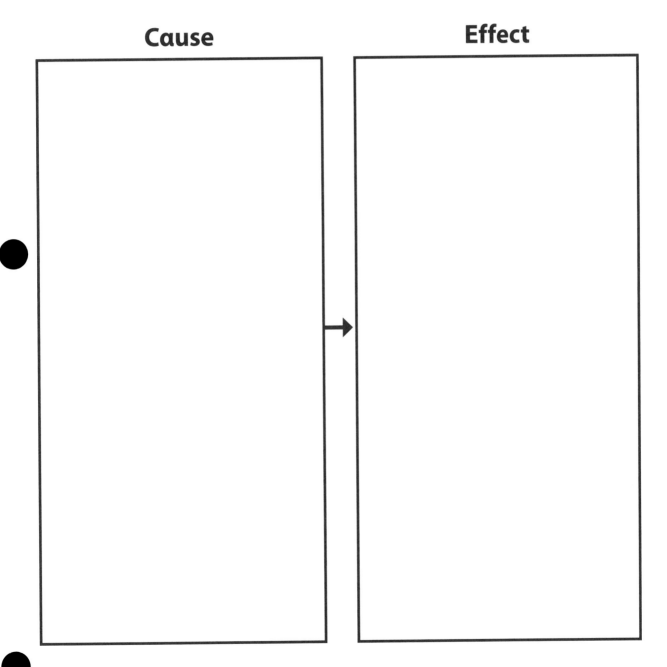

● **Cause-and-Effect Chart**

Cause and Effect

Fill out a cause-and-effect chart to show what happened when you did something.

Cause	Effect

 Tell a partner about what happened and why.

Name _____ Date _____

Words with Long e

Write the word that completes each sentence.

1. theme   Eve

One of my classmates is _____.

2. We   Extreme

_____ like to run each day.

3. she   these

Did you know that _____ runs very fast?

4. egg   athlete

My pal Steve is an _____, too.

5. Concrete   He

_____ pitches to help win games.

6. Pete   be

His pitches can _____ very fast.

7. me   stampede

One day Steve pitched to _____.

8. complete   see

I struck out, but Steve pitched a _____ game!

Name _____   Date _____

Syllables

Write short vowel words from the box under *pen* and long vowel words under *so*.

he	not	no	be	cap	sun
web	him	hi	leg	she	go

pen   **so**

1. _____   7. _____

2. _____   8. _____

3. _____   9. _____

4. _____   10. _____

5. _____   11. _____

6. _____   12. _____

Handwriting

High Frequency Words

Trace each High Frequency Word and then write it.

our our

stop stop

take take

off off

clean clean

let let

think think

going going

●Word Cards: Long e, Short e

me	we	bed	pencil
these	tennis	she	met
bell	Pete	get	here
complete	well	stampede	relax
web	felt	before	wet
decide	he	swell	begin
cobweb	theme	fell	men

●High Frequency Word Cards

other	off
know	going
year	clean
● without	stop
wait	think
warm	our
world	let
● yellow	take

PM3.32

Unit 3 | Water for Everyone

Phonics

● Endings -s, -ed, -ing

Cut out the cards and mix them up. Match the cards and tell how the ending changes the word.

wave	waves
waved	waving
● hop	hops
hopped	hopping
smile	smiles
smiled	smiling

Name _____ Date _____

Mop It Up!

Write a word from the box to complete each sentence.

High Frequency **Words**
clean
going
let
off
our
stop
take
think

1. It is time to _____ our home.

2. I am _____ to help mop.

3. I _____ that is a fun job to do.

4. Mom and Dad _____ me fill the bucket with water.

5. Suds pop up. I turn the water off, but I can't _____ the suds! They go all over!

6. I have to _____ my mop and wipe up the suds!

Grammar: Adverbs

Say Sentences

Directions:

1. Make a spinner.

2. Play with a partner.

3. Take turns spinning the spinner.

4. Say a sentence using the adverb on the spinner.

5. Then your partner says a sentence using the same adverb.

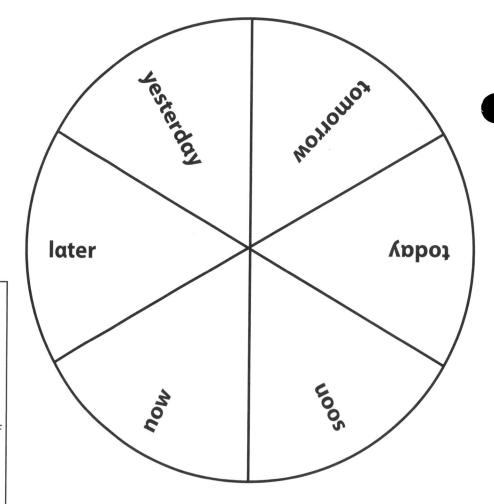

Make a Spinner

1. Put a paper clip ⊂⊃ in the center of the circle.

2. Hold one end of the paper clip with a pencil.

3. Spin the paper clip around the pencil.

● **Phonics**

Endings -s, -ed, -<u>ing</u>

grin + s = grins	bake + s = bakes
grin + n + ed = grinned	grin + n + ing = grinning
bake - e + ed = baked	bake - e + ing = baking

Write the word with the correct ending to complete each sentence.

1. run

Tam is _____ on the path.

2. wave

● She just passed her pal Ben and _____ to him.

3. stop

Ben was skating but had _____ to rest.

4. smile

When Tam ran by, Ben _____ at her.

5. chase

Now Ben hops up and is _____ Tam. Will he catch her?

6. get

The two pals are _____ close to the end of the path.

7. hope

● Tam runs fast and _____ that she will win!

Grammar and Writing

Write Adverbs

Read the letter. Then choose a word from the box that goes with each sentence.

soon	swiftly	yesterday	quickly	slowly

Dear Megan,

Our rafting trip was awesome! I had so much fun _yesterday_.

The river ran _____, but we still tried to paddle. We

sometimes got splashed, but we dried out _____ in the

sun. Now I have to walk _____ because all my muscles

hurt. I hope I can go rafting again really _____, though.

Your friend,

Kate

Cause-and-Effect Chart

Cause and Effect

Fill out a cause-and-effect chart to show the results of things that happened in "PlayPumps."

Cause	**Effect**

Cause	Effect
Kids ride on the PlayPump and turn the wheel. →	

Use your chart to tell a partner about more causes and effects in "PlayPumps."

Phonics

Words with *u_e*

Circle the word that names the picture.

1. mile / mole / (mule)	**2.** cube / cub / cab	**3.** cap / cup / cape
4. fuse / fuss / fist	**5.** fine / fun / fan	**6.** cap / cute / cut
7. use / us / as	**8.** cut / cute / cat	**9.** fun / fame / fume
10. commute / combat / comma	**11.** muffin / mute / munched	**12.** command / compact / computer

Read It Together   Do you think that a mule is cute?

Name _____ Date _____

Phonics

Words with *u_e*

Write the word that completes each sentence.

1. commutes   cubes

Dave _____ to his job each day.

2. dispute   mule

He doesn't ride a _____ to his job in the city.

3. fuse   bus

He rides a _____.

4. fumes   ducklings

On some days, there are a lot of _____ from the bus.

5. Excuse   Truck

One day a man stopped Dave and said, "_____ me."

6. confused   tugged

The man was _____ because he was lost.

7. hundred   used

Dave _____ a map to help the man find his way.

8. shrug   cute

Dave has a _____ little dog.

9. pup   accuse

When Dave is at his job, I take his _____ for walks.

Handwriting

High Frequency Words

Trace each High Frequency Word and then write it.

city city

hold hold

land land

mile mile

much much

river river

sea sea

wash wash

●Word Cards: *u_e*

cube	mule	flute	drum
hut	sun	use	fuse
cute	fume	mutt	tub
put	club	compute	excuse
stuck	include	tube	rude
June	glum	cut	prune
hug	spruce	bun	fun

●High Frequency Word Cards

call	land
more	wash
two	city
● walk	much
than	river
young	hold
why	sea
because	mile
●	

Name _____   Date _____

Compare Information

Use a comparison chart to compare "PlayPumps" and
"The Mighty Colorado."

How People Get Water	
"PlayPumps"	**"The Mighty Colorado"**
• Kids play.	

 Share your chart with a partner. Take turns asking questions about the information.

Name _____ Date _____

More Words with *u_e*

Circle the word that names the picture.

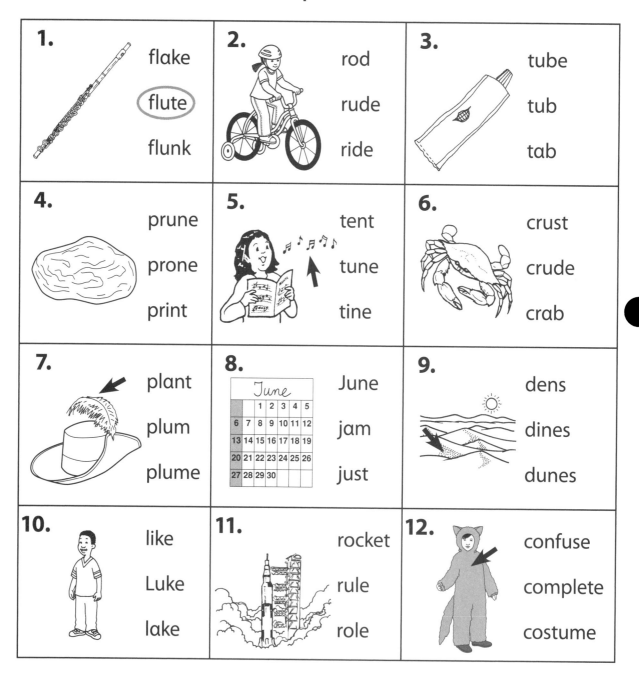

1. flake (flute) flunk	**2.** rod rude ride	**3.** tube tub tab
4. prune prone print	**5.** tent tune tine	**6.** crust crude crab
7. plant plum plume	**8.** June jam just	**9.** dens dines dunes
10. like Luke lake	**11.** rocket rule role	**12.** confuse complete costume

Read It Together One rule is not to be rude.

For use with TE p. T192c   **PM3.45**   Unit 3 | Water for Everyone

High Frequency Words

Home by the Sea

Write words from the box to complete each sentence.

High Frequency Words
city
hold
land
mile
much
river
sea
wash

Can you come to my home in the _____ next June?

There is so _____ to see where I live. If we walk one

_____ to the west, we can walk in the sand by the

sea. Then we can _____ off the sand in the water.

We can _____ hands, jump into the cold water, and

swim in the waves. If we walk the other way, we can see

_____ and water in a _____. I hope you can come

to see me!

Name _____ Date _____

Mix and Match Sentences

First choose a word from column A. Then choose one of the words in column B. Then choose words from column C and say a sentence using all three parts and any other words you want to add. You can change the form of the words in column C if you need to.

A	B	C
I	loud	walk
you	badly	yell
he	quick	write
she	carefully	stop
it	good	play
we	quietly	run
they	well	shout
person	quiet	read
	bad	sing
	quickly	go
	careful	eat
	loudly	fix

Name _____ Date _____

 Phonics

More Words with *u_e*

Write the word that completes each sentence.

1. flutes   dunes

My class is going on a trip to the sand _____.

2. includes   prunes

The trip _____ time for hiking and time for lunch.

3. intrudes   rules

Mr. Chang gave us some _____ for the trip.

4. tunes   costumes

We may sing _____ on the bus, but we may not yell.

5. rude   excuse

We must not be _____ to each other and to people
we see.

6. pollute   plume

We must not _____ while we are there, and we must
take our trash back to the bus with us.

7. assumes   tubes

He _____ that we will be good!

8. mules   concludes

He _____ that if we are good, we will all have fun.

Grammar and Writing

Write Adverbs

Read the letter. Then choose a word from the box that goes with each sentence.

here	there	somewhere	well	smoothly	swiftly

Max was riding on a little raft through the Grand Canyon. The river rushed ___*swiftly*___ through the canyon. The family rafting trip was going _____. After some rough water, the raft was gliding _____ down the river. Max heard a loud sound _____ high over his head. He looked in the sky and saw a big hawk flying up _____. *I cannot believe I am* _____, *thought Max. I am as happy as that hawk must be.*

Adverb Tic-Tac-Toe

1. Play with a partner.

2. Player 1 chooses and reads the sentence. Player 2 tells if the adverb tells how or when.

3. Player 2 marks the square if the answer is correct.

4. Then players switch roles.

5. Keep taking turns to see if one player can get three marks in a row.

The water stopped <u>yesterday</u>.	We <u>quickly</u> called the plumber.	The plumber arrived <u>soon</u>.
The plumber worked <u>carefully</u> to find the clog.	She <u>finally</u> found the clog.	<u>Then</u> she cleared it up.
<u>Slowly</u> the water began to flow.	We have plenty of water <u>today</u>.	We <u>gladly</u> fill our water jugs.

Name _____ Date _____

Phonics

Words with *ai, ay*

Circle the word that names the picture.

1. sell / (sail) / sill	2. ray / rat / rail	3. may / mill / mail
4. ran / rain / rake	5. hit / hail / hay	6. jail / jay / jell
7. chain / chin / children	8. trap / trail / tray	9. bray / braid / brad
10. snack / say / snail	11. paint / pant / pays	12. sprain / spray / sprint

Read It Together Jay paints trains on gray days when it rains.

© National Geographic Learning, a part of Cengage Learning, Inc.
For use with TE p. T201c   **PM4.1**   Unit 4 | Lend a Hand

Name _____ Date _____

Character Traits

Make a character map. Write about two characters you know.

Character	What the Character Does	What the Character Is Like

🗨️ **Tell a partner which character was your favorite and why.**

Name _____ Date _____

Phonics

Words with *ai, ay*

Unscramble the word and use it in a sentence.

1. a h y ___ ___ ___ _____ _____	**2. n i r a** ___ ___ ___ ___ _____ _____
3. i a l s ___ ___ ___ ___ _____ _____	**4. y a w** ___ ___ ___ _____ _____
5. y c a l ___ ___ ___ ___ _____ _____	**6. t i n a r** ___ ___ ___ ___ ___ _____ _____
7. t i w a ___ ___ ___ ___ _____ _____	**8. s l y p a** ___ ___ ___ ___ ___ _____ _____

Name _____   Date _____

Syllables with *ai, ay*

Divide the syllables. Circle the word that names the picture.

1. (raining) resting	**2.** fainted painted	**3.** playing paying
4. mailing rushing	**5.** braided waited	**6.** spraying staying
7. saying sailing	**8.** paying playing	**9.** staying saying

Read It Together   We like playing when it is raining.

For use with TE p. T204f   **PM4.4**   Unit 4 | Lend a Hand

Handwriting

High Frequency Words

Trace each High Frequency Word and then write it.

don't don't

door door

about about

work work

should should

want want

where where

important important

●Word Cards: Words with *ai, ay*

rain	train	hay	spray
aid	sprain	main	yesterday
stain	tray	day	hail
maintain	pail	play	fail
waiting	paid	pain	say
stay	regain	away	plain
delay	decay	pray	always

●High Frequency Word Cards

live	don't
feel	door
water	about
● cold	work
drink	should
turn	want
three	where
● form	important

Name _____ Date _____

Phonics

Syllable Division

Divide the syllables. Circle the word that names the picture.

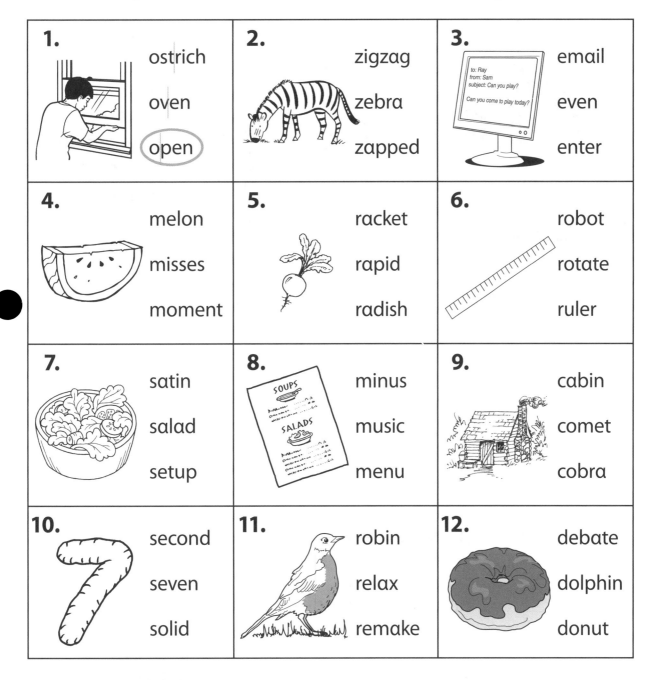

1.
ostrich
oven
(open)

2.
zigzag
zebra
zapped

3.
email
even
enter

4.
melon
misses
moment

5.
racket
rapid
radish

6.
robot
rotate
ruler

7.
satin
salad
setup

8.
minus
music
menu

9.
cabin
comet
cobra

10.
second
seven
solid

11.
robin
relax
remake

12.
debate
dolphin
donut

Read It Together   Is there a zebra or a radish in the salad?

Name _____ Date _____

Who Brings the Mail?

Write a word from the box to complete each sentence.

High Frequency Words
about
don't
door
important
should
want
where
work

1. People who bring mail have an _____ job to do.

2. They _____ hard, and we should thank them!

3. They _____ bring mail on Sundays.

4. My mailman puts mail in the box by my _____.

5. _____ does your mail go?

6. I want to find out more _____ this job because I want to be a mailman!

Grammar: Sentences

Mix and Match Sentences

First choose a naming part from column A. Then choose a telling part from column B. Say a complete sentence using both parts and any other words you want to add.

A	B
girl	tumble
people	save
eggs	snatch
lion	fly
mouse	yell
he	catch
they	go
farmer	help
animals	live
eagle	smash
wall	cry
rocks	chew

PM4.10

Name _____ Date _____

Phonics

Syllable Division

Divide the syllables. Write the word that completes each sentence.

1. frozen   photo

Can you find me in this _____?

2. female   panic

I am the _____ who is playing the trombone!

3. minus   music

I play all kinds of _____ on my trombone.

4. even   exit

I can _____ play some jazz.

5. email   seven

In fact, I will play _____ jazz songs for you!

6. oval   second

The _____ song is the one I like best.

7. moment   bison

Wait for one _____ .

8. begin   panic

Now I will _____ to play.

9. comics   never

I hope that I _____ stop playing my trombone!

Grammar and Writing

Write Complete Sentences

Read the story. Then choose the word or words from the word box that correctly complete each sentence. Write the words.

the little things	somebody
am going to the animal shelter	my sister and I
could not take care of themselves	we

Today I _am going to the animal shelter_ . _____

both help clean the shelter and play with the dogs and

cats. _____ dropped off a box of kittens last

night. The tiny kittens _____ .

_____ mewed loudly and tried to climb out

of their box. _____ picked them up and fed

them from a bottle.

Name _____ Date _____

Aesop's Fables

Make a character map to tell about the characters in
"Aesop's Fables."

Character	What the Character Does	What the Character Is Like
the lion	lets the mouse leave	generous
Farmer Bean		

 Use your character map to tell a partner about the
characters in "Aesop's Fables."

Name _____ Date _____

Words with *ee*

Circle the word that names the picture.

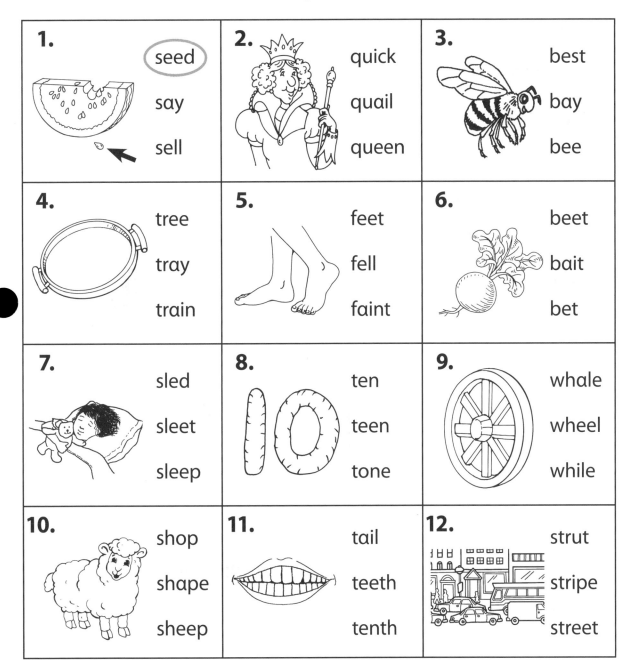

1.	seed say sell	2.	quick quail queen	3.	best bay bee
4.	tree tray train	5.	feet fell faint	6.	beet bait bet
7.	sled sleet sleep	8.	ten teen tone	9.	whale wheel while
10.	shop shape sheep	11.	tail teeth tenth	12.	strut stripe street

Read It Together   Sixteen sheep sleep by the street.

Phonics

Words with *ee*

Write the word that completes each sentence.

1. grin   green

Dad and I sit under a big _____ tree.

2. trip   tree

We see a robin in the _____.

3. cheeps   chaps

It _____ its song.

4. twists   tweets

A second robin _____ back.

5. peeks   seems

My big dog _____ at a log.

6. bets   bees

Look out! There are _____ in the log!

7. leek   lake

My dog runs to the _____ and jumps into the water.

8. creeps   crayons

Then he _____ up to me.

9. slaps   sleeps

He shakes himself off, plops down, and _____.

Phonics

Contractions

I	+ would	= I'd
she	+ will	= she'll
they	+ have	= they've

Write the contraction that completes each sentence.

1. <u>I would</u> like a lemon muffin.

_____ like a lemon muffin.

2. Look! <u>They have</u> got three muffins on a plate.

Look! _____ got three muffins on a plate.

3. I think <u>she will</u> take one plain muffin.

I think _____ take one plain muffin.

4. I see that <u>you have</u> got one nut muffin.

I see that _____ got one nut muffin.

5. I know <u>there will</u> be one lemon muffin left for me!

I know _____ be one lemon muffin left for me!

Handwriting

High Frequency Words

Trace each High Frequency Word and then write it.

house house

kind kind

place place

both both

been been

great great

friend friend

different different

●Word Cards: Words with *ee*

wheel	sweet	bee	feet
she	deeds	he	sweeping
be	eve	agree	feed
beet	we	glee	tree
feel	flee	remix	these
extreme	delete	three	complete
theme	athlete	keep	green

●High Frequency Word Cards

put	house
give	kind
does	place
● away	both
before	been
after	great
through	friend
● carry	different

Name _____ Date _____

Compare Settings and Plots

Use this comparison chart to compare the settings and plots of the two fables by Aesop.

Title	Setting	Plot
"The Lion and the Mouse"	takes place in the forest	
"The Farmer and the Eagle"		

 Share your comparison chart with a partner to talk about the fables.

Name _____   Date _____

Phonics

Words with *ea*

Use paper fasteners and paper clips to
make two spinners. Spin them both and
use the letters to make words below. If
the letters don't make a word, spin again.

Make Spinners
1. Push a brad 𝕏 through the center of the spinner.
2. Open the brad on the back.
3. Hook a paper clip ⊂⊃ over the brad on the front to make a spinner.

Beginning of word   **End of word**

          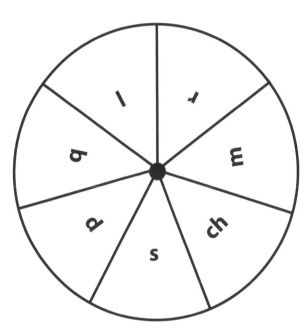

1. chief   5. e a   9. e a

2. b e a k   6. e a   10. e a

3. i e   7. e a   11. e a

4. e a   8. e a   12. e a

PM4.21

Name _____ Date _____

Where Do You Live?

Write a word from the box to complete each sentence.

High Frequency **Words**
been
both
different
friend
great
house
kind
place

1. Lee is my best _____.

2. We _____ live on the same street.

3. My house is _____ from Lee's house.

4. My _____ of house has three homes in it.

5. Have you _____ to my street?

6. It is a great _____ to live!

Grammar: Word Order

Mix and Match Sentences

Choose words from each column and add any other words you need to make a statement. You may use words more than once.

Naming Part	Verb	Object
Mr. Yi	traded	fish
Mrs. Yi	caught	rice
Mr. Jia	shook	soup
They	dropped	bowl of rice
We	made	each other
I	paid	him
She	helped	it

Name _____ Date _____

Phonics

Words with *ea, ie*

Write the words to complete each sentence.

1. beach   daydream

Kim and Jess sit and _____ at the _____.

2. sea   brief

Then they go for a _____ swim in the _____.

3. relief   heat

It is a _____ to get out of the _____.

4. seaweed   real

Kim and Jess find _____ seashells and _____ in the sand.

5. eat   peach

Then they get a _____ and some peanuts to

_____.

6. seagull   steals

A _____ dives down and _____ some peanuts!

7. sneaks   beak

It grabs them with its _____ and _____ away.

8. thief   scream

Kim and Jess _____, "Stop that _____!"

Name _____ Date _____

Write Sentences

Unscramble the words to make a correct sentence. Write the sentence. Use a period.

1. need / help / I / with my homework / .

I need help with my homework.

2. helps / My brother / me / with science / .

_____

3. thank / my brother / I / .

_____

4. help / my brother / I / with the dishes / .

_____

5. each other / We / help / .

_____

Grammar: Complete Sentence

Use Sentences

1. Play with a partner.

2. Toss a coin onto one of the sentence parts below.

3. Put it together with another sentence part to make a complete sentence.

4. Your partner takes a turn.

5. The player who makes the most complete sentences wins.

My friends	make good choices.
are thoughtful.	The teachers
My classmates	give to others.
help me study.	Mom and Dad
Our cousins	show respect.

Phonics

Words with *oa, ow*

Circle the word that names the picture.

1. (row) ray rob	**2.** cot coat kite	**3.** bell bone bowl
4. crow cream crop	**5.** rod road raid	**6.** loaf loft leaf
7. bay bow bee	**8.** got gate goat	**9.** soap seep sip
10. snail snow snob	**11.** boat bait beat	**12.** throne three throw

Read It Together   I see a goat and a crow on the road.

Name _____ Date _____

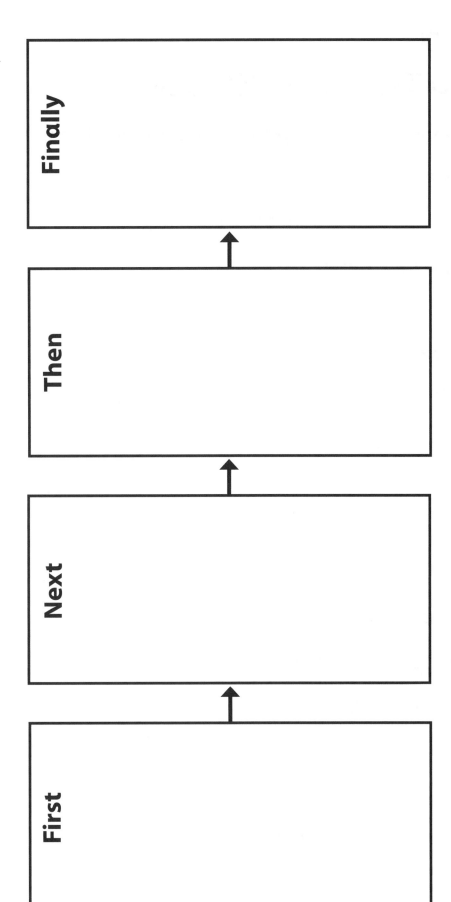

Sequence Chain
Sequence
Fill out the sequence chain to show events in order.

First

Next

Then

Finally

Use the sequence chain to tell the story to a partner.

Unit 4 | Lend a Hand

Name _____ Date _____

Words with *oa, ow*

Write the words to complete each sentence. Then write what it is.

1. window   yellow

It's _____, and it shines in my _____.   _____

2. grows   mow

It _____ fast, so I _____ it.   _____

3. bowl   oatmeal

It's what I do with the _____ in my _____.   _____

4. coat   snows

It's why I put on my _____ when it _____.   _____

5. row   boat

It's a _____ that I like to _____.   _____

6. soaks   rainbow

It _____ me before I see a _____.   _____

7. toast   loaf

It comes in a _____, and I can _____ it.   _____

8. home   throw

I can _____ it over _____ plate for you to hit!

_____

For use with TE p. T232e   **PM4.29**   Unit 4 | Lend a Hand

Name _____ Date _____

High Frequency Words

Trace each High Frequency Word and then write it.

● may may _____

ever ever _____

nice nice _____

● thank thank _____

push push _____

around around _____

teacher teacher _____

● would would _____

●Word Cards: Words with *oa, ow*

boat	toad	window	elbow
bow	floating	toasted	swallow
throw	throat	mow	coast
●moaning	narrow	goat	borrow
road	tow	groan	roadside
grow	row	steam-boat	below
●moat	low	load	slow

●High Frequency Word Cards

off	may
going	ever
clean	nice
● stop	thank
think	push
our	around
let	teacher
● take	would

For use with TE p. T229i

PM4.32

Unit 4 | Lend a Hand

Name _____ Date _____

More Words with Long *o*

Complete the word to name the picture.

1. g(old)

2. b _ lt

3. c _

4. c _ lt

5. h _

6. r _ ll

● **Read It Together**   Can you hold a colt?

High Frequency Words

Miss Gold

Write a word from the box to complete each sentence.

High Frequency Words

| around |
| ever |
| may |
| nice |
| push |
| teacher |
| thank |
| would |

1. Miss Gold is a very nice _____.

2. She may be the best one I've _____ had!

3. I want to _____ her for being so nice.

4. _____ you like to see our class?

5. You can _____ open the door and come in.

6. Look _____. See what makes Miss Gold so nice!

● Word Cards: Subjects and Predicates

the mountain	our hotel	you and I	those photographs
they	most people	a doctor	Alex and Connor
the mayor	her neighbors	children	sheep and cows
help	see	ask	want
hear	eat	visit	make
give	clean up	carry	show
remember	live	play	take

Name _____ Date _____

More Words with Long *o*

Write the word that completes each sentence.

1. folding   strolling

Jo is _____ down the path with her dog.

2. gold   elbow

Her dog looks _____ in the sunshine.

3. window   old

They pass an _____ gate.

4. grow   colt

A little _____ is with a man in the field.

5. holding   soaps

Jo is _____ her dog's leash.

6. scold   both

She uses _____ hands!

7. don't   fold

"I _____ want you to run through the gate and play!" she exclaims.

8. strolling   told

Now Jo and her dog are _____ back home.

9. rolling   cold

Jo is _____, so she wants some hot tea to drink.

Grammar and Writing

Write Subjects and Verbs

Read the story. Then choose a word or words from the box that go with each sentence. Write the word.

the flyer	feel good because I helped a lot of people
our home	sometimes have trouble getting to the grocery store
I	walked around on different floors

Our home is in a big apartment building. I decided

to help some older people in my building. They

_____ .

My dad and I _____ . _____

passed out a flyer with my name and phone number

on it. _____ said to call me and I would go to the

grocery store for them. Many neighbors used my

service. I _____ .

Name _____ Date _____

For use with TE p. T248

Sequence Chain
Giving Back

Fill out the sequence chain to show the order of events in "Giving Back."

First

William Allard sees a boy crying because his sheep have died.

Next

Then

Finally

Tell a partner about the events in sequence.

Phonics

Compound Words

Connect the words to name the picture and write the compound word.

1.

cup

tea ·············· pot

teapot
_____

2.

pack

back

seat

_____

3.

coat

rain

bow

_____

4.

robe

bath

tub

_____

5.

screen

sun

rise

_____

6.

coast

sea

shell

_____

7.

cap

snow

flake

_____

8.

shake

hand

bag

_____

9.

dream

day

time

_____

Read It Together   I look for seashells on the seacoast at sunrise.

Name _____ Date _____

Compound Words

Divide the syllables. Write the word that completes each sentence.

1. sunshine   treetop

The _____ was streaming in through the window.

2. peanut   backpack

Craig got his _____ and helmet to go for a bike ride.

3. homemade   outside

He went _____, but the day was gray.

4. raindrops   weekdays

Then some _____ fell on his nose.

5. daydream   inside

Craig went back _____.

6. beehive   raincoat

He put on his _____ and boots to go out and splash in the rain.

7. sailboat   snowflake

He went out, but a _____ fell on his nose!

8. into   maybe

Craig went back _____ the house for his hat and mittens.

9. snowman   bedside

Now he will go out to make a _____!

Handwriting

High Frequency Words

Trace each High Frequency Word and then write it.

yes yes

say say

says says

write write

dear dear

name name

letter letter

answer answer

●Word Cards: Compound Words

newspaper	eyebrow	goldfish	rowboat
teammate	grownup	walking	blueberry
diagram	sandbox	ladybug	thermometer
watermelon	never	wheelchair	seldom
seaside	cookbook	scarecrow	table
dining	butterfly	sunshine	paper
campfire	tattoo	towels	footprint

●High Frequency Word Cards

land	yes
wash	say
city	write
● much	dear
river	name
hold	letter
sea	says
● mile	answer

Name _____ Date _____

Compare Author's Purpose

Work with a partner to fill in the comparison chart.

Author's Purpose	William Allard	Carol Jordan and Arwa Damon
to persuade		
to inform		✓
to entertain		
to share experiences	✓	
to tell about other parts of the world		

 Which selection did you like best? Share your opinion with a partner.

Phonics

Abbreviations

Cut out the cards and mix them up. Match the words to the abbreviations and use them in sentences.

Mister	**Mr.**
Doctor	**Dr.**
Street	**St.**
Road	**Rd.**
Sunday	**Sun.**
April	**Apr.**

● **High Frequency Words**

Mittens

Write a word from the box to complete each sentence.

High Frequency Words
answer
dear
letter
name
say
says
write
yes

● _____ Gramps,

We got a kitten! Her _____ is Mittens. When

I say "Mittens," she has an _____ for me. She

_____, "Mee-oo."

May Mittens and I visit you? I hope you say,

"_____!" Will you _____ me a letter? Tell me if

we may visit.

Your grandson,

Jake

●Word Cards: Subject-Verb Agreement

the boys	our house	Shannon and I	those CDs
they	you	the newspaper	my friends
the pilot	some players	a child	a dog
wait	says	run	makes
jump	eats	talks	think
chooses	tell	drives	hope
hear	takes	watches	gets

Phonics

Abbreviations

| Monday → Mon. |
| Mark Joseph Smith → M. J. Smith |

Write the word that completes each sentence.

1. **Mrs.   St.**

   My mom is a teacher. Kids call her _____ Chan.

2. **Wed.   Mr.**

   My dad is a teacher, too. He is _____ Chan.

3. **Dr.   Rd.**

   Mom's class is going on a field trip
   to see a vet. The vet is _____ Gray.

4. **St.   Sun.**

   The kids get on the bus at 27 Pine _____ at 10 a.m.

5. **Oct.   Rd.**

   They get off the bus at 9 Hancock _____ at 10:30.

6. **Nov.   Ms.**

   They see the date Friday, _____10 on the vet's door.

7. **Mon.   P. C.**

   The vet shows them Mr. _____ Mason's cat.

8. **Ave.   Feb.**

   Mr. Mason and his cat live on Prescott _____ next to me!

Write Verbs That Agree

Read the story. Then choose a word from the box that correctly completes each sentence. Decide if you need to add *s* or *es* to the verb.

| feel | help | relax | take | wash | work |

My mom is a hero to me. She __works__ at a hard

job to support my brother and me. Sometimes she

_____ very tired after work and does not feel like

playing with us or fixing dinner. Then my brother

and I _____ as much as we can. We _____ the

dishes. My brother _____ out the trash. Finally, my

mom, my brother, and I all _____ .

Name _____ Date _____

Use Subject-Verb Agreement

Grammar Rules Subject-Verb Agreement

Every sentence has two parts: the subject and the verb. The subject and verb must agree.

The boy wait**s**.

one person

Parents smile.

more than one person

1. Partner 1 points to a subject card.

2. Partner 2 points to a verb card.

3. If the subject and verb agree, cross out both cards.

4. Play until all the cards are crossed out.

Subject Cards			
Avi	Teresa	Mr. and Mrs. Mendez	You and I
He	She	They	We

Verb Cards			
wants	builds	helps	hopes
work	study	need	carry